The Twelve Month Pregnancy

by the same author

The Allergy Cookbook

STEPHANIE LASHFORD

THE
12
MONTH
PREGNANCY

YOUR DIET,
FROM PRE-CONCEPTION,
TO MOTHERHOOD

with illustrations by

KETHRINE KNIGHT

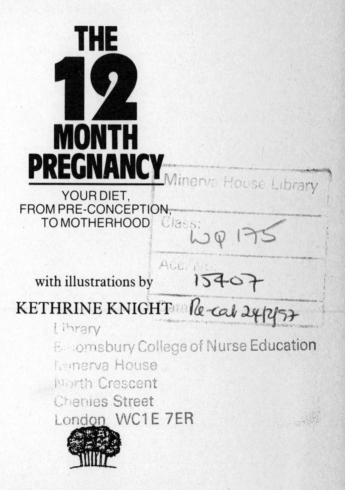

ASHGROVE PRESS, BATH

Published in Great Britain by
ASHGROVE PRESS LIMITED
26 Gay Street
Bath, Avon BA1 2PD

ISBN 0 906798 41 8 (hardcover)
ISBN 0 906798 42 6 (paperback)

First published 1985

Photoset in Plantin by
Ann Buchan (Typesetters)
Walton-on-Thames, Surrey
Printed and bound in Great Britain by
Adlard & Son Ltd, Dorking, Surrey

for Richard and Suzanna

the two most important little people
in my life

ACKNOWLEDGEMENTS

Professor Brian Hibbard – for his help and guidance
Professor Michael Laurence – for capturing my imagination
for this subject
Dr Andrew Lashford (my husband) – for keeping me going!
Margaret Foster – for helping with the preparation of the script
Dr Jim Hayes – for advice and direction on the diabetic section
Dr Nansi James – for help in collecting the research material
And everyone else who has helped me along the way

Contents

FOREWORD

'Eat for two' is granny's traditional advice to prospective mothers but unfortunately this is usually interpreted as an abundance of carbohydrate and calories. Whilst it is true that energy demands do increase in pregnancy, the real needs are for a sufficiency of proteins, vitamins and certain minerals which are essential to the healthy formation of the two billion or so cells of the baby about to be born. Stephanie Lashford has translated these needs into some exciting recipes from which a good pregnancy diet can be constructed.

The early weeks of pregnancy are crucial. It is at this time that the vital organs are forming and the baby's needs for good building blocks for the foundation of later health and development exist, even before you realise you are pregnant – that's why it is important to get yourself in trim *before* pregnancy. Then the baby, from the moment it embeds in the wall of your womb, when it is only a week old, has the best possible environment. More and more obstetricians and couples planning a pregnancy are recognising the benefits of a *preconception* regime which includes, as well as good eating habits, health checks and a positive approach to physical fitness.

In the developed Western world an average diet *should* provide suitable amounts of all the nutritional essentials. For various reasons it in fact often falls short of the optimum, not because of poverty or basic ignorance but because of pressures of work, the availability of quick convenience foods and the ability of a food technologist to disguise products to make them attractive to the eye and to the taste buds but disappointing to the body's metabolism. Of course not all modern food processing is detrimental. The nutritional value of margarine may well be better than natural butter and deep frozen foods are often preferable to last week's limp 'fresh' vegetables.

Pregnant women are often encouraged to take dietary supplements – iron tablets, vitamin preparations etc. – but tablets can only provide a limited and incomplete range of nutritional needs. It is much better to get biochemical necessities for you and your baby from the greengrocer and the butcher rather than the pharmacist and it needn't be expensive. That's what this book is all about. Just look at some of the recipes. Wouldn't you prefer *Fandango* or *Spiced liver with orange* to gelatine coated capsules of iron and vitamins? Not only are the recipes good for the mother to be, they are also suitable for all the family and especially for growing children. So why not start now,

1

whether you are pregnant or just hoping to be in the not too distant future?

Professor Bryan Hibbard MD Ph.D FRCOG
Professor of Obstetrics & Gynaecology
University of Wales College of Medicine

INTRODUCTION

I hope this book will help all prospective parents to understand the importance of diet during pre-conception and pregnancy. It has given me immense pleasure to write this book and I have met some exceptional people whilst researching the material for it.

There is one point that I should make clear from the outset: this book cannot help those people who are having difficulty in conceiving. There is a multiplicity of reasons for this which diet can never hope to alter, and it would be irresponsible of me to suggest otherwise.

I hope you will find this book interesting and informative and a useful aid to good nutrition, and may I wish all prospective parents much joy and fulfilment in your new adventure.

Stephanie Lashford

PRE-CONCEPTION CARE

Will good eating habits ensure that I conceive?

Unfortunately we do not have any proof to date that confirms that good eating habits will ensure conception. But we can draw several valuable conclusions about how inadequate nutrition affected pregnant women and their babies in times gone by.

Some of the most reliable accounts of the effects of severe malnutrition during pregnancy are those of the famines that occurred during World War II.

During the siege of Leningrad, which lasted from August 1941 to January 1943, many thousands died from starvation. The effects of food shortage were evident within a few months of the start of the war, and the average birth weight of infants carried to term was reduced by approximately 500 grams. Almost half the infants born in the following year weighed less than 2.5 kilos.

Another well documented famine affected cities in Western Holland in the winter of 1944. Fortunately the deprivation was less severe than that encountered in Leningrad. It lasted six months and was preceded and followed by periods of adequate food supply, so mothers did not experience severe nutritional deprivation for the whole duration of pregnancy. Babies who were exposed to famine conditions during the final months of pregnancy showed the greatest loss of birth weight, whereas those whose mothers had had adequate food supplies in late pregnancy were of normal weight.

These findings are consistent with the rapid growth of the foetus in the last three months of pregnancy (Widdowson, 1980). Experiments on animals have also confirmed that malnutrition is more undesirable for the birth weight of the foetus in late rather than early pregnancy (Morgan and Naismith, 1977).

The most important feature of both famines as far as conception was concerned was the dramatic increase in the incidence of loss of periods (amenorrhoea) in the young female population, directly linked to a shortage of foodstuffs. During the last four months of the Dutch famine the number of infants conceived fell to one half of the previous conception rate (Stein et al, 1975). Similar observations were made in other European cities at the time. For example, in Frankfurt the birth rate fell to 30% of the previous level during 1944 and 1945 (Navjoks, 1949). Because of the wealth of information from these periods in

4

history available to doctors, two researchers, a husband and wife team by the name of Wynn, have drawn some interesting conclusions to support the idea that an improved eating pattern is an essential aspect of pre-conception care. They have brought to attention the vital importance of sound nutrition around the time of conception, particularly with reference to congenital malformations which originate in the first two months of pregnancy. During this time important foetal development takes place. In support of their arguments they point out the striking rise in the frequency of prematurity and infant mortality with the Dutch famine which did not occur among infants born during the food shortage, but among those born several months later who had actually been conceived during the food shortage (Stein and Sausser, 1975).

The findings of the famine studies suggest that while malnutrition in the latter part of pregnancy affects actual birth weight, in early pregnancy it affects the capacity for survival and development.

Although these findings are in the extreme and one hopes they will never be repeated, they are nevertheless very valuable. They reinforce the theory behind good eating habits before and after conception and show us what severe malnutrition can do. So we must try to ensure that all women who want to bear children are well nourished before and during pregnancy, which in turn should result in a greater reduction in problems both during and after pregnancy. Women who are well nourished and having regular periods are more likely to conceive than malnourished women with an irregular menstrual cycle. This is why I have placed so much emphasis on the three month pre-conception stage, during which any nutritional problems and deficiencies can be rectified before actual conception and a good eating pattern established. By using the advice and recipes given in this book you are well on the way to a happier and healthier pregnancy.

What is pre-conception care?

Pre-conception care is taking a long look at yourself and deciding how to improve your general health by changing your eating habits and taking adequate exercise. It is designed to give you a better chance of a healthy pregnancy and an enjoyable delivery. Although I cannot give any guarantees with this book I hope I can help you come to understand what your body needs before and during pregnancy and how to provide the best for it. By entering into this 12-month pre-conception and pregnancy diet you will have three months in which to get yourself into a positive frame of mind, to provide yourself

5

with a healthier body to begin your pregnancy and nine months of the pregnancy to let your body do the job you want effectively.

You may decide you want to discuss particular problems you have during the three month pre-conception period with your G.P. or perhaps whilst on a visit to the hospital chosen for your confinement. Some hospitals do offer pre-conception counselling where you may even have a medical examination and a blood test. It would certainly give you peace of mind knowing all is well, if not there would be an opportunity to put things right before you actually conceive. I am sure any doctor would prefer you to have a clean bill of health before you conceive rather than sorting things out once you are pregnant.

Exercise is another very important aspect of pre-conception care, and during the 3 month pre-conception period I want you to follow some kind of exercise programme. You do not need to start on the regime of an Olympic athlete but do start a programme to suit your life style. Any sport which you enjoy and which you can fit in on a regular basis will do, as long as it is not too strenuous and time consuming, as your very good intentions could fizzle out quickly! Walking rather than taking the car, going to Keep Fit classes, or, my favourite, the Women's League of Health and Beauty. The latter has a friendly approach and holds several classes on different levels so that they can offer something for everyone. Also worth reading is the *Body Plan Book* which I followed quite recently through a series in the *Sunday Times*. It proved very interesting and would be useful to anyone who has never taken regular exercise. I liked it because it starts you off very sensibly, taking things very slowly to begin with and then gradually building up over a period of time. It also has some interesting ideas about food. Swimming is good exercise to start with, especially if you are over-weight, and it is pleasurable even when pregnant, as long as all is well. Yoga is also a good form of exercise for toning your muscles and, as it is coupled with exercises to help you learn the art of relaxation and an understanding of your body, it will introduce you to the different ways of relaxing and breathing which are a great asset during labour. Many of the exercises taught in ante-natal classes are based on yoga principles.

Pre-conception care may sound new and unfamiliar but it does have something to offer all women who want to have a baby.

Here is, I hope, a well thought-out list of adjustments which can be made to your lifestyle to improve your health and well being, during the pre-conception stage and during pregnancy itself.

1.   Choose tinned goods carefully – although when appropriate and

possible buy and use fresh foods. Some tinned goods are acceptable and can often enhance a meal or dish. Canning can also be advantageous, as in the case of red kidney beans which need to be boiled to render poisonous toxins safe. This is done during the canning process. Baked beans are a useful addition to a healthy diet since they are a source of protein and fibre and are relatively cheap. Coupled with toasted wholemeal bread and a low fat spread they provide an almost balanced meal.

2.   Avoid too many packeted savoury extras – those which provide a variety of flavours and come in exotic shapes and colours. These are empty calories and are not part of a healthy diet. If you really need some extra nibbles try nuts, raisins and those delicious mixes you can buy in the health food shops, full of toasted seeds, sun dried pineapple and papaw.

3.   Whilst following the 'get healthy for pregnancy' programme put your frying equipment to the back of the cupboard and try grilling, baking and steaming instead and using lots of raw food recipes. It's extra nutrients you need, not extra calories.

4.   Having a sweet tooth is something you personally have developed. You can lessen or considerably reduce it by providing alternatives to take away your cravings. You can either eat less calorific savoury foods or, another good way is to do somthing you enjoy to take your mind off your yearnings. Gentle exercise is another plus and should help you on your way to keeping within the 20 pounds allowance for a pregnancy weight gain.

5.   Your attitude to methods of cooking is as vital to your good health as the very foods you choose to eat. It is no good buying the very best quality fresh foods and then cooking them to death. I have given this matter a good airing in the section on how to get the most from the food you buy. One final point here is: on *no* account add bicarbonate of soda whilst cooking any vegetables. I should think any green vegetable catching sight of a bicarbonate packet would have instant heart failure! It leaches out any water-soluble nutrient into the water which is inevitably thrown down the sink – an utter waste of any goodness. A simple remedy is perhaps not to cook most vegetables at all!

6.   The question of alcohol. My own personal answer is this: you have lots of time to enjoy wine and alcoholic beverages later, after the birth of the baby, so giving up for this short time, which is definitely considered better for the unborn child, should be thought about carefully and kept to. So yes – no alcohol – and you will see from

the recipes that food can be delicious without alcohol. You yourself will also derive immense benefits in improved health by abstaining from it. When attending social functions there is a wide range of delicious non-alcoholic drinks available now, so take advantage of them.

7.   As part of a health-conscious eating programme you would be well advised to change from sweet, sticky, highly-coloured drinks, such as pop and squash, which provide only calories, to fresh fruit juices or orange and lemon cordials which are colour and preservative free and calorie reduced.

8.   We are all sufficiently educated now to know that smoking is undesirable and even more so when following a health conscious programme for pre-conception and pregnancy itself. You must therefore make a conscious effort to give up smoking and not to spend long periods of time in smoky atmospheres. One of my own personal concerns about smoking during pregnancy is that prospective mothers smoke rather than eat.

Basic components of a pre-conception and pregnancy diet

1.   Choose foods that are in season – because they are usually cheaper and at their best then. Their nutrient content will be substantially greater than other produce that has had to travel great distances.

2.   When you have a choice – choose foods that have not been processed. Processed foods may be nutritionally adequate but they may also contain artificial preservatives, colourings and flavourings which are not part of a healthy diet.

3.   Aim to eat a variety of foods – do not eat the same foods day after day otherwise you will be limiting your intake of nutrients. Each foodstuff contains its own individual nutrients – so *variety* will give you the nutritional *balance* that is essential.

4.   *At each meal eat at least one of the following foods:*
a)   *Meat* – alternate between red and white meats e.g. pork, lamb and beef are red; chicken, turkey and veal are white.
b)   *Fish* – choose a different type each week and choose unprepared fresh or frozen fish rather than that ready prepared which probably contains additional preservatives and colourings. Remember that such fish as mackerel and herring are valuable because they contain the important vitamins A and D.
c)   *Eggs* – these can be made into very simple meals such as poached

8

egg on wholemeal toast or become part of a more exotic dish for special occasions. They are very handy in emergencies.

d)   *Cheese* – is a rich source of fat and fat soluble vitamins, so try a different variety each time for a difference in taste and texture. Ideally keep to three cheese based meals per week, as cheese is high in calories. Try Edam which is relatively low in calories (only 88 calories per ounce, (25 gms)), or cottage cheese which can be used in a variety of ways to give interest to low calorie meals.

e)   *Liver and kidney* – it is essential you make an effort to eat one or the other each week. There is a great variety of offal that people are often unaware of and some very tasty dishes to prepare using it. You need not stick to just one type, there is ox or pig's for those who enjoy a stronger, very distinct flavour and lamb's, calf's, chicken or turkey for those who prefer a more delicate flavour. Liver and kidney can be made to taste delicious on their own, but those with an absolute dislike can simply disguise them within a dish they enjoy and will truly never be able to detect their presence. Try liver, for instance, liquidised in Spaghetti Bolognaise or Chili con carne.

5.   *Vegetables and Salads* – you should have at least two different *fresh* vegetables each day. Do not stick to the same two but try as many different ones as possible. It should be two other than potatoes, preferably the green leafed varieties such as brussel sprouts, mustard and cress, sea kale, water cress, lettuce – all types, endive, asparagus, spinach, sorrel, cabbage – all types, spring greens, broccoli and kale, all of which are very rich in folic acid, a very important component of this diet. Potatoes themselves should always be cooked and served in their jackets as the Vitamin C content lies just below the surface and their skins should preferably be eaten and not removed.

6.   *Fresh fruit* – you should aim to have fresh fruit every day, winter and summer alike. It is important that you eat a variety of fruits. For example, peaches and nectarines are cheaper and at their peak during the summer, so enjoy them whilst in season. It is important for a healthy diet to eat at least two different fresh fruits daily.

7.   All bread, cakes, pastry and biscuits should be either wholewheat or wholemeal. You should avoid wherever possible anything containing white flour. Wholemeal and its products are superior in every way.

8.   All the cereals – breakfast cereals and any others that you have as part of your diet – should be prepared from whole grains.

9.   Do have at least one pint of milk each day. Yoghurt can be substituted if necessary but only eat natural, unsweetened varieties.

SUGGESTED MENUS FOR ONE WEEK

	Breakfast	*Lunch*	*4 p.m. (Tea)*
Monday	French toast grilled tomatoes	Cheese and Chickory Brunch wholemeal roll fresh fruit – coffee	Florentine Meat Loaf brown rice and butter bean salad
Tuesday	Careba with 5 fl oz (150 ml) milk one banana chopped and mixed in coffee	Quick Liver Sausage Salad Yoghurt	Thatched Fish and Mango Pie sweetcorn, jacket potatoes cheese and an apple
Wednesday	Muesli – home-made with 5 fl oz (150 ml) milk one piece wholemeal toast – coffee	Quick Processor Pate 4 Ryvita and ½ oz (10g) vegetable margarine 1-2 slices melon 1 packet of dry, roasted peanuts	Chinese Beef fried rice Orange and Banana Mix
Thursday	poached egg on toast fruit juice	a slice of quiche lorraine one tomato and cucumber slices 4-6 oz (110g-175g) grapes - washed before eaten	Beef with Red Kidney beans Green Spinach Salad 2 oz (50g) Edam Cheese 3 sticks of celery
Friday	2 oz (50 g) salmon on wholemeal toast grilled tomatoes coffee	quick cheesy rolls one wholemeal roll buttered three baby beetroots fresh fruit (in season)	Liver Persian Style brown rice, yoghurt dip one ripe mango – sliced

Saturday	4 oz (110 g) cottage cheese on wholemeal toast with half a fresh peach coffee	Leek and Watercress Soup one wholemeal roll one muesli bar (bought from a health food shop)	Scampi Provençale jacket potatoes, broccoli and carrots Banana and Strawberry Brulée
Sunday	one kipper fillet one slice wholemeal bread and butter tea/coffee	Pot Roast Beef with Horseradish à la maison jacket potatoes, Swiss Cabbage, cauliflower Malted Rice Pudding	Mixed Livers Pâté sandwiches Mixed Berry Royale Sugar-free fruit and nut Gingerbread

WOMEN WITH SPECIAL NEEDS

What pre-conception care can offer to women who are under-weight

Being under-weight during pregnancy is just as undesirable as being over-weight and can bring with it a number of problems. Women who are under-weight give birth to babies who have a low birth weight and so the baby may experience difficulties which in turn cause undue stress for the mother.

It is difficult in this fashion-conscious age actually to make people believe that it is possible to be under-weight. Some people get a real phobia about it. This is a condition called anorexia nervosa, which needs special medical help. Furthermore, many women strive to be slim and spend much of their time on slimming diets. Although one may remain slim it is a recognised medical fact that being under-weight leads to reduced fertility.

Some fad diets where only a few foods are eaten can also be problematic and if you were to conceive whilst on one of these diets you could run the risk of being malnourished, which is most undesirable.

It is very important, if you are under-weight, that during the three months before conception you alter your diet. By using the recipes and menu plans in this book you will provide yourself with an abundance of nutrients which will give you the building bricks with which to build a new life. If you don't feel totally satisfied with your health then a check-up with your doctor who will be able to answer your questions should put your mind at rest.

It is important that you bring your weight back up to your natural weight and that you feel fit and healthy.

Here is some basic advice for an under-weight woman to follow in order to gain weight to return to her natural weight during her three months leading up to conception.

1.   Have regular, well balanced meals with plenty of variety. Use as many different types of food as possible.

2.   Avoid heavily fried or sugary foods which are empty calories. This means they are calories only and provide hardly any other nutrients.

3.   Use fresh foods, e.g. fresh meat and fish and lots of fruit and vegetables.

4.   Take regular exercise to encourage a healthy appetite and to promote well being.

5.   The use of wholemeal products would be advisable because they are nutritionally superior to white flour products. These include bread, cakes, pastry, pasta and rice.

What pre-conception care can offer to the overweight woman

You can be overweight but still be undernourished, for you store excess fat when overweight, not excess nutrients. It is the nutrients you need when you become pregnant, not extra pounds. Being overweight in pregnancy can lead to other complications too, high blood pressure, hypertension and eclampsia.

If you are in trim this means your muscles are in good working order; and if you take exercise regularly your labour should be an easier affair – as it's your muscles that do the work during labour. Muscles that are flabby find the job much more difficult so that women who are overweight and not fit may find that doctors need to intervene by delivering the baby by Caesarean. This does mean an increased risk because of the use of anaesthetics, and particularly for the mother, not having the pleasure of being awake when baby arrives.

Being overweight also means that during your pregnancy your doctor will have difficulty in feeling the baby through all those layers of extra fat. So by reducing weight you will assist the doctor in his ability to help you! One interesting point I discovered during the research for this book is that when a woman is overweight it hides her real body type and shape. This knowledge can be important for a doctor when considering certain types of medication during pregnancy and at birth itself.

By following the advice in this book for changed diet and exercise programmes a woman should find herself in a fitter state when delivery time arrives which in turn should enable the muscles to do the job in hand more effectively for her.

Entering into the 12 month pre-conception and pregnancy diet can assist the overweight woman to change her eating pattern three months before the egg and sperm meet. By changing to the sort of foods I recommend in this book and undertaking a sensible exercise programme during the three month period before conception you will give yourself a great bonus and something which I'm sure will warm the heart of your G.P., obstetrician and midwife. I'm positive he/she would be pleased to see you taking a very active and positive step to helping yourself and in the long term your baby too.

Doctors are very reluctant to prescribe a calorie reduced diet once a woman is pregnant because it is a time when she needs to feel at one with the world and also needs a varied and balanced diet. There are also so many other changes going on inside the body that it is not a good idea to introduce too many fundamental new ideas at this time. But by reducing your calories and not your nutrients during the three month pre-conception period you are going to find getting your figure back once the happy event is over a much easier task.

Basic outlines for someone who feels they want to lose weight during the pre-conception stage

1.   Reduce your fat consumption by 50% (this includes all the hidden fat in bacon, sausages, beefburgers, etc.). Change from animal fats to vegetable fats which are rich in unsaturated fats.

2.   Reduce your sugar consumption by at least 50%. This also includes the hidden sweetness in tinned fruit in heavy syrup. Change to fruit canned in natural juice.

3.   If you feel you need extra help, contact a weight watching organisation. It could give you support and extra advice for the pre-conception stage.

4.   Take some exercise. Begin slowly and work towards a regular routine. The *Body Plan Book* which was serialised in the *Sunday Times* is a good introduction for those women who are new to the exercise game.

5.   The use of wholemeal products would be advisable as they are nutritionally superior to white flour products.

What pre-conception care can offer to women who must have a gluten-free diet

It is possible that you have been following a gluten-free diet for some time and have already gathered together a selection of delicious dishes to make, and feel fit and healthier with this eating programme. But once your nutritional demands alter, to prepare your body for pregnancy you will have to reassess your eating programme. This I have attempted to do for you and have provided a selection of recipes that you can use along with your usual ones to provide a diet that will look after your personal needs during the pre-conception stage and during pregnancy itself.

What is gluten?
Gluten is a protein that is found in wheat, rye, barley and oats. It is found only in grains, with the exception of rice which can therefore be used to replace the other carbohydrate foods in your diet.

Where do you find gluten?
It is found mainly in bread, cakes, biscuits, pastry and breakfast cereals. It is also hidden in some ready-prepared products to thicken them, make them smooth and to help bind the other ingredients together.

Are there foods without gluten?
All vegetables and fruit, meat, fish, pulses, eggs, cheese, milk, butter, margarine, oils and nuts are gluten free. These nutritious foods can be transformed into delicious dishes to keep you healthy on your gluten free diet.

What flour can I use?
Commercially prepared gluten reduced flours, where most of the gluten has been taken out, are available. There are also some naturally gluten-free flours. These are potato flour, soya flour, pea flour, rice flour, and maize flour, otherwise known as cornmeal.

What pre-conception care can offer diabetic women

The pre-conception stage allows you time to discuss the implications of being pregnant and a diabetic with your hospital doctor and your own G.P., who will advise you on all important aspects. The three month pre-pregnancy period will enable you to discipline yourself into maintaining a very well controlled diabetic eating programme and you can use the recipes in this book along with the ones you already use to meet the new demands made on your body once you become pregnant.

FOODS WHICH PLAY AN IMPORTANT PART IN A HEALTHY DIET

Proteins

Protein foods are an essential part of a well-balanced programme of eating. They are the building blocks of life and are used for growth and the repair of damaged tissue. They promote the development of the mother's uterus, breasts and increased blood supply during pregnancy and should be eaten at each meal. Balance and variety is particularly important.

Foods rich in proteins

Meat
Fish and shell fish
Cheese
Eggs
Milk and Yoghurt
Dried Peas and Beans
Macaroni – noodles and spaghetti
Breakfast cereals – generally those that are wheat based
Bread – generally the wheat flour variety
Rice and products
Corn and products

Fats

The more fat you eat in excess of your daily requirements the more you store. This is laid down in the body as adipose tissue.

The fats you eat in your diet can be divided into two basic types – Saturated fats and Unsaturated fats – which differ in how their atoms are joined together. It is part of modern day thinking that a diet rich in unsaturated fats is better for you. These fats are mainly derived from vegetable sources. It is important, even if you are following a calorie-controlled diet, to have some fat in your diet otherwise important vitamins needed cannot be absorbed.

Foods rich in fats

Dairy produce – milk, cream, cheese, eggs and butter
Meat – beef, lamb
Oily fish
Pork and products, e.g., bacon,
sausages
Margarine
Oils – all types e.g. corn, peanuts, almond, coconut, etc.

Carbohydrates

Carbohydrates are important in a diet to provide energy. If

insufficient are consumed then the proteins eaten are used instead for energy purposes thereby starving the body of protein needed for cell growth and repair. As a guide you should have one carbohydrate-rich food at each meal, remembering to keep the serving 'average'. This is important as only small amounts are stored in the liver and in the muscles, giving only up to eight hour's supply for moderate activity.

Foods rich in carbohydrates

Cereals, e.g. pearl barley, oat-meal

Rice

Spaghetti, etc.

Lentils

Haricot beans

Flour and all products made from flour

Sugar and all products from sugar

Sultanas, prunes, dates, figs, dried apricots

Chips

To a lesser extent milk and its products

Facts you should know about vitamins

Through medical research we now know a great deal about vitamins and the important role they play in supporting good health. Vitamins are found in many different foods and in varying amounts. As they are easily destroyed (e.g. by heat and light) it is important to have a variety of foods and eat these foods as fresh as possible. If you follow this advice you should not need to take vitamin pills since a good, well balanced diet will provide you with all the vitamins you need.

Vitamin A

Vitamin A is stored in the liver in large quantities and therefore a deficiency is very unlikely. It helps in preventing infection by keeping mucous membranes in good order. It is necessary to assist cell formation and to develop bones and teeth, specially the enamel on an unborn baby's teeth. It is also necessary for normal vision. Vitamin A is fat soluble.

Foods rich in Vitamin A

Dairy produce, which includes eggs, milk, yoghurt, cheese and butter

Soya milk

Margarines – these are all forti-fied

Carrots, spinach, watercess, tomatoes, peas, lettuce,

pumpkin, sprouted vegetables

Liver – is extremely rich

Kidney

Prunes, apricots – especially eaten dried

Melon

Oils – salad and cooking varieties

Vitamin B
As there are several members of the Vitamin B family it is usually referred to as the B-complex. They are all important and have their own particular job. If you have a well balanced diet with ample variety you should not need to take supplements. You should aim to have all the foods stated which are rich in Vitamin B as part of your normal eating pattern.

Foods rich in the B-complex
Meat – red types contain the most, white varieties are low in Vitamin B content, so only eat occasionally
Fish – traces found in most varieties, so vary your fish types
Yeast spreads – miso, marmite
Seeds and beans – soya, peas, black eyed beans, red kidney beans, chick peas (garbanzo peas) sesame, sunflower seeds
Brown rice and whole grains, rye in particular
Pulses, lentils in particlar
Fresh, dark green vegetables, e.g. broccoli, brussel sprouts, spinach, kale, lettuce, endive, asparagus
Alfalfa, beansprouts – or any sprouted vegetables. Chinese supermarkets are good places for ideas
Folic Acid (Vitamin B9) is also found in oranges and bananas

Vitamin C
Vitamin C should be eaten daily as it is not readily stored in the body. A severe Vitamin C deficiency results in a condition called scurvy, which in modern times is very rare. Vitamin C is used in the body to cement cells together. It helps promote healing, and builds up resistance to infections. It may also assist in the absorption of iron, which is important during pregnancy.

Foods rich in Vitamin C
Those with the highest Vitamin C content are brussel sprouts, cauliflower, red and green peppers, blackcurrants. Foods with a moderate Vitamin C content are strawberries, oranges, lemons, limes, pomello, tangerines, grapefruit, spinach, raw cabbage and gooseberries. Foods which are eaten in relatively large amounts and on a regular basis provide a contribution to adequate vitamin C intake. Such foods are potatoes, raspberries, melon, broad beans, runner beans, frozen peas, tomatoes.

Vitamin D
Vitamin D is stored in the liver and also manufactured by the fatty

17

tissue in the skin when exposed to sunlight (ultra-violet light). It has an effect on the body's ability to absorb minerals, in particular calcium and phosphorus. Vitamin D is essential for bone formation and the hardening (calcification) of the bones. A severe vitamin D deficiency could result in a condition called rickets, but with a well balanced diet this would be most unlikely. Vitamin D is fat soluble.

Foods rich in Vitamin D
Herrings, kippers, tinned salmon, sardines
Margarines – they are fortified
Natural products containing vitamin D, e.g. milk and butter, have higher Vitamin D levels in the summer than in winter months. This is because the cows can eat fresh green grass in the summer which is not available during the winter. Vitamin D levels in dairy products may therefore vary.

Mineral Salts

If you have a balanced diet with ample variety you will derive all the mineral elements your body needs wihout resorting to supplements. These minerals are needed in trace amounts only and by simply applying good common sense to your meal planning you should not become deficient in any of the minerals your body needs to be and stay healthy.

Two of the important minerals which are worth discussion and needed during pregnancy are Iron and Calcium.

Iron
You need extra iron in your diet during pregnancy because your blood volume increases by 25% and the baby develops its own store from your supply to last him/her several months until solids are introduced. It is vitally important that you have foods rich in iron during pregnancy. There are other foods besides liver to top up your iron levels.

Foods rich in iron
Liver – all types and other organ meats such as kidney and heart
Cocoa powder and products derived from cocoa
To a lesser extent dried apricots, almonds, desiccated coconut, haricot beans, sardines and most red meats

Calcium
Calcium is needed in a pregnant woman's diet because it provides the basis for sound bones and teeth in the developing baby, and also helps

maintain the mother's own bones and teeth. By adopting a balanced and varied diet you should derive all the calcium you need.

Foods rich in calcium
All milk and milk products such as skimmed milk, hard cheeses such as Cheddar and Gruyere, Yoghurt
Fish where the bones are eaten, e.g. sardines, whitebait
Cereals, e.g. wheat and wheat products, wheat germ, bulgur flour, rice, soya flour
Treacle

Fibre

Although strictly not a nutrient, fibre is necessary to assist the passage of food through the digestive system. It is particularly important in pregnancy as your muscles can become lax, and to avoid constipation and more so piles, you should eat a diet with an increased fibre content. Foods that are rich in fibre are vegetables and fruits complete with edible skins, peas, beans and legumes, e.g. baked beans, whole grains, nuts – and the ever famous bran.

Water

Water is taken in by several ways, e.g. in food and drink but you should ensure that you drink regularly and do not have drinks that are sugar ladened.

If you have lead water pipes make sure you do not drink from the hot taps as the hot water dissolves the lead from the pipes and it is not desirable to drink this. Run water from the cold taps in the morning so that any water which has been standing over night is got rid of, as some lead may have dissolved into the water. This problem is becoming less important as copper piping is now used; my comments only apply to those living in old houses.

PLANNING MEALS

I really do feel that not enough information is readily available on how to plan economical and nutritious meals. It is rather taken for granted that once you are an adult you automatically know the do's and don'ts of planning meals or even why you should bother to plan at all. It is of vital importance when preparing yourself for pregnancy that you take a new look at what you eat and how you plan your food so that you eat a good variety of foods and in the correct *balance*. This is what pre-conception care is all about – getting your body into good order for the job you want it to do.

As any organiser will tell you, an event that is not well planned is often incomplete and unsatisfactory; people are only too ready to comment on how unsatisfactory something is when it's inadequate and fails to stimulate. Take, for example, a play. It may be a well written piece of work, but without the correct planning and organisation it will be unsatisfactory to both the actors and the audience. The same can be said for meal times – a meal that is ill-prepared is unsatisfactory for both the cook and the people eating it. So it is vital that however simple or plain the foodstuffs used may be, the meal must be well planned.

How do you put this advice into action? All my meals are planned and organised long before I reach the shop doorway. And now I will explain how you too can help yourself to obtain better value from the food you buy and eat.

Every Friday morning I take two sheets of paper and a pen and a cup of coffee and sit down. One sheet is headed 'menus for the week' and the other 'shopping list'. On the menu sheet I write down the days of the week and then work out the meals needed and leave blank those to be eaten out. I then decide what type of meal each is going to be, bearing in mind the events to be fitted in to our busy week: e.g. Richard to swimming lesson, husband to meeting, Suzanna to birthday party and so on. This is to ensure that I am not going to purchase more than I need and also reduces wastage – a very important factor in these times of high costs. I then consider what we ate last week and try not to have the same pattern as this creates boredom, which is something to avoid at all costs. Questions I ask include: 'How much money do I have this week?' 'Am I entertaining?' and 'Is this week going to have to be a cheap one?'. If the latter, I tend to bake to reduce costs, and I even bake my own bread when needs be.

	Breakfast	Lunch	Tea
Saturday	Muesli	A sausage in pitta bread coleslaw yoghurt and fruit	boiled eggs soldiers scones and preserve
Sunday	grilled bacon, tomatoes and mushrooms	baked lemon chicken jacket potatoes mixed lettuce salad compôe	salmon sandwiches mixed berry royale date and walnut loaf
Monday	careba and yoghurt	*packed lunch:* pâté sandwiches natural yoghurt 1oz raisins 1 orange	beef with red kidney beans brown rice fresh fruit
Tuesday	muesli with fresh fruit and yoghurt	*packed lunch:* salmon rolls portion coleslaw 2 sticks celery 1 apple	vegetable pizza and cheesy coleslaw fresh fruit
Wednesday	boiled eggs and toast	*packed lunch:* flask soup wholemeal roll with ham 1 banana	quick processor pâté wholemeal rolls fresh fruit
Thursday	citrus starter	*packed lunch:* 4 oz cooked meat portion salad 4oz grapes	quiche lorraine tofu coleslaw orange and banana mix
Friday	poached egg on toasted wholemeal muffins	*packed lunch:* peanut butter sandwich natural yoghurt 2 plain biscuits 4 ozs cherries	oven baked fish with tartare sauce jacket potatoes beans and sweetcorn apple crumble and custard

It does not mean that because less money is spent the meals provided are less nutritious. On the contrary, they are often of more nutritional value, as I tend to be extra careful in my choice.

Having got to this stage I then decide if I have anything I want to use up in the cupboards or freezer or is there something to use from the garden e.g. rhubarb, spinach?

From the menus chosen I make a shopping list of only those items I know I am going to use and this stops me buying little extras on impulse. Advertisers spend a great deal of time creating ways to make housewives buy on impulse. They usually concentrate on items surplus to requirements so beware – and do not fall into the trap. This is particularly important when trying to get yourself into good shape, for you do not want to gain extra pounds during a pregnancy. As many of the items bought on impulse are packeted luxury good such as small fondant cakes or chocolate biscuits instead of plain ones, they are often poor in nutrient quality and also high in cost per item. If you were to spend the same amount of money thus spent on fruit or home-baked items you would derive much greater nutrient value for your money. Advertisers are really quite naughty in that they insinuate that by buying such sweet items you are expressing your love for your family and they use high-pressure psychological techniques to get you to buy them. It is difficult to avoid this but armed with a shopping list you should be able to resist such lures and enticements and buy only what is strictly necessary.

The pace of life – the pace of life is usually quick for most of us so the preparation of food needs to be as quick and simple as possible, yet at the same time providing very good nutritional value. Many prepared meals advertised imply that they give you freedom from your kitchen. To be seen enjoying yourself in the kitchen, even preparing the simplest of meals is portrayed as dull and unfashionable. But do remember that cooking is a craft, a skill and can and should be enjoyed at all levels. You do not have to be a gourmet to gain satisfaction from food preparation. I like to encourage everyone to reach their own potential. Preparing food is important and it can be relaxing and a form of unwinding for many, especially if your partner will make it a joint effort. So go ahead, enjoy yourself in the kitchen and look upon cooking as a creative art, not a chore. With your planned menus and well-chosen items you will have extra time to enjoy yourself and have a healthier diet into the bargain.

Here is some practical and useful advice on how to get the most from the food you buy

1. Using raw vegetables and fruits for salads and desserts ensures that you obtain the maximum amount of nutrients from the food. And as they are quite expensive it does seem much more sensible to eat them this way. I have made a conscious effort when devising the recipes to keep the nutrient content as high as possible.
Here are some tips to help you get the most from your vegetables:

(a)   Buy them as fresh as possible and do not buy them for the whole week but buy them as you need them, for they lose vitamins by the hour once they have been picked. Otherwise you are just wasting money.

(b)   Prepare them as you need them. Once you start chopping and washing you expose them to the air, destroying those vital vitamins.

(c)   Cook them for as short a time as possible in a small amount of water. You can improve matters by
  (a)   cooking the vegetables in a dish where the liquid is eaten as well e.g. Goulash, Hot Pot
  (b)   steaming them – there is a revival in this method of cooking and steamers are now more readily available.
  (c)   keeping the liquid to make a gravy or sauce, ensuring none of the nutrients go to waste.
  (d)   stir frying – in a very small amount of fat is also a very good way of ensuring vitamins in vegetables are conserved and also makes them very palatable.

2. I think selecting fruits and vegetables that are in season is a very sensible idea, no matter how many exotic fruits they may fly in from across the world. There is nothing quite like local grown new potatoes nor the succulent taste of a sun-ripened English tomato. As soon as a fruit or vegetable is picked it starts to lose its nutritive value and the two important nutrients that are lost are Vitamin C and folic acid. Therefore the further they have to travel and the more they are handled the more the nutrients are destroyed. If they have to then spend a day travelling to market and another day before they reach the shops and then perhaps a day or so in your vegetable rack how much of the Vitamin C and folic acid is left? Not very much!

3.   Fresh, canned and frozen fish are less expensive than some meats as a general rule. You can also make economies on the grades of fish you buy – for example, a salmon pâté could be made from pink salmon whereas a salmon salad is better suited to red salmon.

4. Poultry, which includes chicken, turkey and poussins, has become cheaper in recent times and is quite versatile. But unfortunately it falls short in nutritional terms, as one of the important nutrients a woman needs during pre-conception and pregnancy is folic acid. Chicken and white meat are a poor source of this. They therefore cannot be recommended as a main protein source, only as an extra.

5. As an alternative to animal protein eggs, peanuts and peanut butter, dried peas and beans are a pleasant change and can be cooked in so many different ways. As an interesting comparison, one egg, one ounce of cheese (25 g), two heaped tablespoons of peanut butter give the same amount of protein as one ounce (25 g) of meat. I will leave you two work out the difference in cost! So remember a variety of all foods is necessary to give you economy and nutritional balance.

Always compare the cost of various sizes of eggs, remembering that 1 is the largest and 7 the smallest. I was very surprised when I recently made a note in all my local shops of prices and found as much as 12p/doz. difference for the same size egg. And, of course, there is no nutritional difference between brown and white eggs. This depends upon the breed of hen and what the farmer has been feeding them on. In America they have a preference towards white eggs whereas we seem to prefer brown eggs!

Here are some points to consider in order to get the most from dairy foods
(a) Buying milk from the supermarket is cheaper than from the doorstep.
(b) Using dried skimmed milk in cooking and baking gives the important nutrients from milk, but reduces the total calorific content of a dish.
(c) Use English cheese as opposed to foreign – again for economy.
(d) In terms of nutritive value received from cream, cream cheese and ice-cream are the more expensive dairy products so value for money for nutrients would mean the use of yoghurt, milk, English cheese and butter.

Are you getting the most from the meat you buy?
(a) I always consider the cost per serving. Large amounts of bone, gristle and fat in a piece of meat may increase the cost per serving of lean meat. A good comparison to make is one pound (450 g) of lamb cutlets will feed two people whereas one pound (450 g) of brisket made into a pot roast will serve four people.
(b) Liver, kidney and heart are good buys. Pig's and Lamb's liver and kidney are much less expensive than calf's and are just as

nutritious. Ox and pig's liver have a much coarser texture and a stronger flavour and are suitable for pâtés whereas lamb and calf's liver have a finer texture and more delicate flavour and are suitable for casseroles and frying.

(c) Make the meat stretch by making it into stews, casserole dishes, creamed dishes and meat loaves.

(d) Look around in the butcher's – do not just stick to your usual routines. You need variety in your diet and it is also an excellent opportunity to introduce new meat dishes. So have a good look next week! Pork, lamb and occasionally veal may be better buys than beef. And using the recipes in this book will enable you to create a whole new gastronomical world for yourself and your family!

Here are some tried and tested ways of getting the most from your shopping and your food

1. Watch out for weekly special offers and take advantage of them in menu planning – but do not buy just for the sake of buying.

2. Ensure you have your shopping list with you. It's of no use whatsoever left on the kitchen table. Avoid the temptation of purchasing expensive luxury goods that are not part of a health conscious diet. Also be prepared to make substitutions when food of equal nutritional value is available much more cheaply. See the list of foods and their respective nutritional values elsewhere in the book to familiarise yourself with the important ones.

3. Use the larger supermarkets for your weekly/monthly shopping as they buy in huge quantities and are usually cheaper than the small independent shops. Also larger supermarkets have a quicker turnover and you will be able to eat fresher foods.

4. Read the labels on tins and packets and come to understand them. Learn to discriminate between what is good nutritionally and what is not. The sensible choices are foods which are made from pure ingredients and contain little sugar or fat, and are without preservatives and colours. Many products do state that they are without preservatives or added colour. They are much better to have as part of a healthy diet. Products made from wholemeal flour are nutritionally superior to those made from white flour, so make your choices wisely.

The people you cook for rely on your judgement to provide them with the best both from the nutritional point of view and that of gastronomical delight and pleasure.

2

5.   Purchase in large quantities e.g. large tins of baked beans if the price per unit is less. Once you start doing this you will get very good at it. Do remember that you should be able to store the food bought satisfactorily and that it should be used before it perishes.

6.   Remember once you have purchased any item of food especially any fresh fruit and vegetable you must consider how you are going to store it. You would be amazed at how quickly the nutrients disappear, especially Vitamin C and folic acid, if stored for too long. It is sheer waste to purchase good quality food and not to use it quickly. Ideally you should buy vegetables and fruit daily.

7.   To ensure you do not waste food at the table try to cook it in a manner that will provide the most pleasure from eating it. Serve attractively and in the size portions you know are likely to be eaten. Then the family do not feel pressurized into eating more than they want or can manage and you do not get annoyed and frustrated because the effort you have put into the preparation and organisation and the money you know you have spent have been wasted. Tension at the dinner table is very off putting.

8.   What do you do for yourself at mid-day? Do you grab something on the way and then hope for the best? Now that you are considering producing a new life it is vitally important that you have a nutritious mid-day meal. You must have a protein food and preferably a salad or fresh vegetables, with a sensible afters of an apple, banana or a yoghurt. I always take my food with me, then I know that I am having a sensible lunch. Food eaten out at a restaurant or bought from a sandwich bar is much more expensive and you cannot always count on its freshness and nutritional value.

9.   Getting the most from your food is very important and I do not think that we give it sufficient emphasis. For example, knowing what to cook at any one meal is very important and here are a few ideas on how to get it right:-
      (a)   Use your money wisely; good nutrition is not always expensive. It just takes *thought*.
      (b)   However much time you have – use it well. Do not be over ambitious when time is short. Raw foods only need to be washed and trimmed; oven baked foods such as baked sausages, chicken portions, casseroles, jacket potatoes can be cooking, using an oven timer, whilst you are out at work or picking up the children.

      Bake when you have any spare time and pop the result into the freezer – put a pastry base in the fridge when you have time, to make into a quick quiche for tea.

Once you start getting yourself organised you will get better at it. Lazy minds do not produce good wholesome food.

(c)   The time of the year is important. You should aim for hot and filling meals in the winter and mixed (hot/cold) and lighter foods in the summer.

(d)   Consider the age and sex of the people you are cooking for. Each age group has its own special requirements and the groups that are most vulnerable and need the most assistance are 'the young', 'the mother to be' and 'the elderly'. There are several other groups to consider such as the manual worker and so on, but I want to emphasise the requirements of 'the mother to be' which we shall deal with in great detail within this book.

GUIDE TO FOODS IN SEASON

Fruit	*Home Season*	*Imported Season*
Apples, dessert	September-May	all year
Apples, culinary	September-June	all year
Apricots		December-January & June-August
Avocados		all year
Bananas		all year
Cherries	July-August	April-September & November-December
Cranberries		all year
Grapefruit		all year
Grapes		all year
Lemons		all year
Kiwifruit		all year
Mangoes		all year
Melons		all year
Oranges		all year
Passion Fruit		all year
Peaches		June-September & December-February
Pears	August-March	all year
Pineapples		all year
Plums	August-October	December-April & June-October
Pomegranates		September-December
Rhubarb	December-July	
Soft Citrus		all year
Strawberries	April-October	September-June

Vegetables	Home Season	Imported Season
Artichokes, Globe		all year
Artichokes, Jerusalem	October-November	all year
Asparagus	May-June	September-May
Aubergines	May-October	all year
Beans, Runner	July-October	all year
Beans, French	June-September	all year
Beans, Broad	June-July	April-June
Beetroot	all year	March-July
Brussels Sprouts	August-March	few in winter
Broccoli	all year	November-June
Cabbage	all year	all year when required
Carrots	all year	all year
Cauliflower	all year	all year when required
Celery	all year	January-July
Chinese Leaves	April-November	November-March & May-July
Courgettes	June-October	all year
Cucumbers	March-October	all year
Fennel	August	June-March
Leeks	August-May	
Lettuce	all year	all year
Marrow	June-October	April-July
Mushrooms	all year	
Okra		all year
Onions	all year	all year when required
Parsnips	August-April	
Peas	June-September	
Peppers	May-October	all year
Potatoes	all year	all year when required
Radishes	all year	all year when required
Spinach	April-November	November-April
Sweetcorn	August-October	November-February
Swedes	September-May	
Tomatoes	April-October	all year
Turnips	all year	April-June
Watercress	all year	

Eating Out

You may find yourself during the pre-conception stage and pregnancy in many situations where you have no alternative but to eat out. My advice to you in such situations is – pick your foods carefully. There is no need not to eat at all, you would be well advised to have something rather than nothing.

Here is a list of types of food to go for when eating out:

Salads – served with cheese, cold meat, eggs
Omelettes
Beefburgers – without chips
Pizzas – preferably with a wholemeal base
Ploughman's Lunch
Sandwiches – preferably made with wholemeal bread with either chicken, tuna, pâté, peanut butter, turkey, sardines or cheese.
Coleslaw and raw vegetables
Fresh fruit – or a fresh fruit salad
Yoghurt
Cheese and biscuits

Drinks

Milk
Milkshakes
Mineral water
Fruit juices
Vegetable juices

Avoid fried and greasy food and alcoholic drinks

SICKNESS IN PREGNANCY

This seems to be a problem for most women, and the first trimester and the third trimester are possibly the worst. I suffered for most of my 2 pregnancies with sickness, which was often sparked off by cooking smells rather than anything else. Being a Home Economics teacher it was very difficult indeed, and so I tried many different ways of warding off the sickness.

Here are some ideas from myself and other mums on our ways of getting over sickness

1.   Have a cup of tea in bed with dry toast or plain biscuits before getting up.
2.   Carry a bottle of soda water and digestive biscuits in your hand bag in case you feel sick when out.
3.   Cold crispy apples eaten slowly. Sit down whilst you do this and try and relax.
4.   Salt and Vinegar crisps and Perrier water (not too many crisps because of the calories).
5.   Toasted wholemeal honey sandwiches eaten with your feet up.
6.   A cup of hot milk with a teaspoon of maple syrup and a good pinch of cinnamon (also said to be good for heartburn).
7.   Never having large meals, but taking several simple and light meals throughout the day.

A final word: follow your instincts and have a little of what you fancy.

WHAT TO DO ONCE BABY HAS ARRIVED

You can still use this book as an aid to continued good nutrition, and if you choose the dishes that are low in calories it will help you to loose any extra pounds you may have gained during pregnancy.

If you are going to breast feed your baby, which I would personally recommend as the best for any baby, also use this book to give you balanced nutrition whilst lactating.

Once you start to wean your baby the recipes in this book will be useful because they are nutritionally well balanced and if liquidised will provide an excellent diet for any child. Remember to omit the salt as all food for babies must be low in salt. Salt puts an unnecessary load on young delicate kidneys. Their food may seem bland to your taste buds but will be perfectly adequate and acceptable to them.

As a general guide from then on eat well, but try to develop savoury tastes rather than sweet, and enjoy a very mixed diet. The same rule applies – variety and balance.

BREAKFAST

As a nutritionist I always say you should have a good breakfast; such a breakfast is vitally important now that you wish to carry and feed a new life inside you. Breakfast is particularly important because after a night's rest the body's reserves are low and need to be replenished.

BREAKFAST RECIPES

1. Compôte au Muesli
2. French Toast
3. Blender Breakfast
4. Citrus Starter
5. Careba
6. Pancakes
7. Muffins

The Best Way to Start the Day?

The traditional English breakfast of bacon, eggs and fried bread gives adequate protein but rates too high in fat content. What you need is a meal that gives ample protein, all the B vitamins including folic acid, vitamins A, D, C, E, iron, calcium and other important trace minerals. It does not matter from where you get these nutrients as I found during my own pregnancy when I fancied cheese or salmon on toast in the morning. Even if you stick to similar things each morning it does not matter as long as they contain the essential nutrients.

We have seen quite radical changes in the types of breakfast cereals available and you should take advantage of them. There are high fibre cereals, sugar free ones and a whole range of others with added vitamins which with the addition of milk or yoghurt are a complete meal in themselves. However, I would urge you to make up your own muesli and granolas so that you do not have the additives that may be in manufactured ones.

1. *Compote au Muesli*

This is an exotic dish which makes an excellent topic of conversation with guests over breakfast. I often have it for Sunday breakfast when I have sufficient time to prepare and eat it at my leisure whilst enjoying the paper and breakfast T.V.

Serves 6

Ingredients:

½lb (225 g) winter fruit salad comprising dried apricots, peaches, pears, prunes and apple
4 oz (110 g) raw cane sugar
6 oz (175 g) rolled oats
2 oz (50 g) flaked almonds
2 oz (50 g) chopped hazelnuts freshly toasted under the grill or bottom of the oven
2 oz (50 g) rye flakes
enough milk to mix to a soft consistency

Method

1.   Soak the winter fruit salad for 2 hours or overnight. Discard the water. Cover with fresh water and add 2 oz (50 g) of the sugar. Simmer until the fruit is tender and nearly all the liquid has evaporated.

2.   Place in the fridge to chill.

3.   Place the rolled oats, remaining sugar, rye flakes all together in a mixing bowl and add sufficient milk to make a soft consistency.

4.   To this add the chilled compote and mix.

5.   Serve in individual bowls and top with the freshly toasted, warm nuts. Excellent before your Sunday morning jog, or after if you prefer!

2. *French Toast*

Makes 4 portions

Ingredients:

8 slices wholemeal bread
3 eggs, size 2
pinch of salt
top of the milk
2 tablesp. vegetable oil

Method
1.　Beat the eggs in bowl and add the salt and top of the milk. Beat again all together.
2.　Dip the slices of bread in the mixture.
3.　Heat the fat and sauté the bread until brown on both sides.
4.　Place on a warmed plate until all the slices are cooked.

Serve in a variety of ways
1.　On its own with grilled bacon and tomatoes.
2.　Spread with cottage cheese or cream cheese.
3.　Spread with marmalade.
4.　Spread with honey and a pinch of cinnamon.

---

3. *Blender Breakfast*

This is very good when you are feeling a little off colour in the morning and do not feel like anything solid. Taken with a wholemeal biscuit or muesli bar it will provide a fairly balanced meal with which to start the day.

Ingredients:

2 or 3 fresh apricots – tinned ones will do
½ pint (275 ml) pineapple juice

1 egg, size 1 or 2
1 tablesp. clear honey

Method
1.　Place all the ingredients in the blender and blend until smooth.
2.　Serve in a tall glass.

---

4. *Citrus Starter*

An excellent dish with which to start the day, rich in Vitamin C, and topped with a breakfast cereal such as Jordans Original Crunch to add sweetness and extra nutrients.

Serves 4-6

Ingredients:

1 pomello
1 tangerine
1 sweet orange
4 tablesp. granola type breakfast
  cereal

1 grapefruit
1 small fresh pineapple *or* a small
  tin of pineapple tinned in natural
  juice
½ pint (275 ml) fresh orange juice

Method

1.   Peel and segment the pomello, tangerine, orange and grapefruit and place in a glass serving bowl. Chop if the segments are too long.

2.   Peel and remove the centre of the pineapple and chop into bite size pieces. Add to the bowl (or add the tinned pineapple).

3.   Pour on the fresh orange juice and mix well.

4.   Chill. Top with a granola breakfast cereal served from a separate bowl for everyone to help themselves.

---

5. *Careba*

This breakfast cereal can also be called a granola which means a selection of ingredients baked or toasted before serving. There are many variations available and you can even be adventurous and invent your own.

Enough for 12 servings

Ingredients:

2 oz (50 g) flaked almonds
2 oz (50 g) pecan nuts
2 oz (50 g) hazelnuts
1 oz (25 g) sesame seeds
12 oz (350 g) jumbo oats

8 oz (225 g) clear honey
2 tablesp. soya oil
4 oz (110 g) desiccated coconut
1 teasp. vanilla essence

Method

1.   Chop all the nuts up coarsely. Add the sesame seeds, jumbo oats and desiccated coconut.

2.   Stir in the honey, vanilla essence, and soya oil and mix very well.

3. Spread the mixture onto two oiled baking trays and bake for 20 minutes at Gas Mark 4, 350°F, 180°C until evenly brown. Turn during baking to obtain an even colour.

4. Allow to cool and then store in a sealed container and use within 3 weeks. Serve for breakfast with milk and some chopped fresh fruit, e.g. banana or peaches, for an unusual breakfast.

---

6. *Pancakes*

The French invented them, the Americans took them on and they are a great favourite for breakfast. They are very quick to make in the morning and with a nutritious filling are a substantial way to start the day. To save time in the morning, prepare the night before. They are especially quick to make when made in a liquidiser or food processor.

Here are three different recipes for you to try using different flours and milks to provide interesting and delicious varieties of texture and flavour.

TRADITIONAL PANCAKES

Makes 4-6

Ingredients
2 size 4 eggs
½ pint milk (275 ml)
4 oz (110 g) unbleached flour

pinch of flour
oil for frying

WHOLEFOOD STYLE PANCAKES

Makes 4-6

Ingredients:
2 eggs, size 4
½ pint (275 ml) soya milk
4 oz (110 g) wholewheat,
   buckwheat or barley flour (or

even a mixture of all three to give
  an interesting and varied taste)
pinch of cinammon
oil for frying

Method – By Hand
1.   Place the flour in a mixing bowl and add the salt (or cinnamon if making wholefood pancakes).

2.   Make a well in the centre and drop in the eggs.

3.   Add just enough milk (4 tablesp.) to incorporate all the flour. Stir until smooth.

4.   Add the remaining liquid gradually.

5.   Tip the mixing bowl slightly and beat using the back of the spoon. This is to incorporate as much air as possible.

6.   Place in the fridge until required.

Method – Using a Food Processor
1.   Place all the ingredients (using cinammon for wholefood pancakes – salt for traditional) into the food processor and utilising the twin blade attachment process for 5-7 seconds.

2.   Place in the fridge until required.

FRENCH PANCAKES (CRÊPES)

Makes 4-6

Ingredients:

4 oz (110 g) unbleached flour
pinch of salt
2 eggs – separated
½ pint (275 ml) milk

1 tablesp. of honey
grated rind of one lemon
oil for frying

Method

1. Place the flour and salt in a mixing bowl.

2. Add the egg yolks and honey and beat in half the milk.

3. Whisk to incorporate as much as air as possible.

4. Place the egg whites in a separate bowl and whisk until stiff. Then whisk in the lemon rind.

5. Fold the egg whites into the batter mixture using a metal spoon.

6. Use immediately.

How to cook pancakes and get good results

1. Heat enough oil to coat the bottom of the frying pan. Pour off any surplus.

2. Pour enough batter to make a thin layer over the base of the pan.

3. Cook until lightly golden (half a minute).

4. Turn – by either tossing or using a fish slice – and continue cooking until golden brown.

5. Turn onto a warmed plate and place in a low oven.

6. Continue until all the batter is used.

If you cook too many at once you can freeze the remainder. Pack individually with cling film, then pop into a freezer bag. To reheat place on a baking tray and bake at Gas Mark 3, 325°F or 170°C until warm.

For savoury dishes use either the traditional or wholefood style pancake recipes. French Pancakes are strictly for sweet dishes.

Nutritious fillings for breakfast pancakes

1. Thick set natural yoghurt with ground almonds and sultanas.

2. Tofu, stewed apple and cinammon.

3. Mashed banana and honey.
4. Sugar reduced and preservative free jam.
5. Clear honey and chopped nuts.
6. Honey and lemon juice.

7. *Muffins*

For a change from ordinary toast, try muffins. They are very nice toasted with egg, bacon, cheese or marmalade. I would recommend the whole wheat variety for those extra B vitamins and fibre. There is more to a muffin than an ordinary piece of toast! For an even more unusual taste try this American interpretation of the age-old English muffin.

AMERICAN STYLE MUFFINS

Makes 1 dozen

Ingredients:

8 oz (225 g) Polenta (corn meal)
6 oz (175 g) wholemeal self raising
  flour
2 oz (50 g) raw cane sugar
3 level teasp. baking powder
a good pinch of salt or salt
  substitute

2 eggs, size 2
1 oz (50 g) vegetable fat
1 oz (50 g) vegetable margarine
melted and cooled
½ pint (275 ml) butter milk
(ordinary milk will do)

Method

1. Place the Polenta, wholemeal flour, sugar, baking powder and salt (or salt substitute) into a large mixing bowl and stir well.

2. Beat the eggs well and then add the melted fat and buttermilk.

3. Make a well in the flour and pour the liquid. Mix with a metal spoon until smooth.

4. Pour into oiled pattie tins, individual yorkshire pudding tins or a loaf tin (1 lb – 450 g size).

5. Bake for 20-30 minutes at Gas Mark 6, 200°C, 400°F.

SNACKS
AND
LUNCH-TIME MEALS

It does not matter how simple the snack or
lunch-time meal is itself provided it is well
balanced nutritionally. These recipes have
been devised so that they are quick, simple
and nutritious.

SNACKS AND LUNCH-TIME MEALS RECIPES

8. *Quick Liver Sausage Salad*

Serves 1

Ingredients:

1 large carrot – grated
1 medium sized apple – chopped
1 tablesp. raisins
2 teasp. lemon juice
3 tablesp. natural yoghurt

a pinch of salt and pepper
4 oz (110 g) diced liver sausage
3 lettuce leaves or half a bunch of
   watercress

Method

1.   Blend the lemon juice, yoghurt, salt and pepper together.

2.   Add the grated carrot, chopped apple, raisins and liver sausage.

3.   Place the lettuce leaves or watercress in a plastic container or on a plate and pile on the dressed salad.

Serve with wholemeal bread.

9. *Winter-time Salad*

Serves 1

Ingredients:

2 cooked and diced potatoes
2 cooked and diced beetroots
2 oz (50 g) defrosted peas
2 tomatoes
2 chopped gherkins
4 oz (110 g) tinned asparagus
4-6 oz (110-175 g) shredded
   cabbage

Dressing:

2 hard boiled eggs
3 tablesp. cider vinegar
¼ pint (150 ml) top of the milk
1 teasp. sugar
a pinch each of salt and pepper

Method

1.   Slit the eggs and reserve the whites as garnish.

2.   Pound the yolks, add the seasoning, cider vinegar and sugar and top of the milk. Mix well.

3.   Add the diced potatoes, beetroots, peas, tomatoes, gherkins and asparagus and mix well.

45

4.   Place the shredded cabbage in a container or on a serving plate and pile the salad on carefully.

Garnish with the chopped egg white.

---

10. *Cheese and Chicory Brunch*

Serves 1

Ingredients:

4 oz (110 g) cottage cheese
1 oz (50 g) cheddar cheese – cubed
1 tablesp. natural yoghurt
1 teasp. lemon juice
pinch of cayenne pepper

1 oz (25 g) chopped walnuts
one small tin of pineapple rings in
    natural juice
2 small heads of chicory

Method

1.   Prepare the dressing by combining the yoghurt, lemon juice, and cayenne pepper and then mashing in the cottage cheese.

2.   Stir in the cubed cheddar cheese and walnuts.

3.   Wash and shred the chicory and place on a plate and arrange the pineapple rings in the middle of the plate.

4.   Into each pineaple ring pile the cheese mix and garnish with a dash of cayenne pepper.

Serve with wholemeal bread.

---

11. *Beansprout and Sausage Diner*

Serves 1

Ingredients:

4 oz (110 g) washed beansprouts
4-6 sprigs watercress – chopped
1 carrot – grated
3-4 oz (75g-110 g) black grapes –
    de-seeded and cut into halves
4-6 oz (175 g- 225 g) Cumberland
    sausage – cooked and cooled (any
    spiced sausage may be
    substituted)
2 lettuce leaves

Dressing:
2 tablesp. cider vinegar
2 tablesp. soya sauce
½ teaps. sugar
2 teasp. sesame seed oil

Method
1. Dice the cooked Cumberland sausage into bite sized pieces and place in a mixing bowl.

2. Add to this the washed beansprouts, watercress, carrot and black grapes and mix.

3. Prepare the dressing by combining the cider vinegar, soya sauce, sugar and sesame seed oil in a small bowl. Pour over the mixed ingredients and coat well.

4. Shred the lettuce and arrange on a plate and pile the salad in the centre.

Quick, delicious and very nutritious!

---

12. *Quick Processor Pâté*

An ever increasing number of woman have food processors and it is important to make the most of them. This paté is so quick and simple to make that it is an excellent standby for snacks, packed meals and even dinner parties if you want to add some cream to give a fuller flavour.

Serves 8-10 portions

Ingredients:
4 medium smoked mackerel fillets
4 oz (110 g) butter – melted
juice of a large lemon

Method
1. Skin the mackerel and break it up.

2. Place in the processor and using the twin blade attachment process for 5-7 seconds.

3. Add the melted butter and lemon juice and process for a further 5 seconds.

4. Transfer into a 2 pint (1.1 litre) bowl and chill.
Serve with oatcakes, toast or with celery.

Oily fish such as mackerel and kippers are a good source of vitamins A and D – vital for good vision and the healthy growth of bones and teeth. These vitamins are stored in the liver if eaten in excess so a daily intake is not vital.

47

13. *Rumaki*

An hors d'oeuvre that is always a hit even if you are not a liver lover.

Serves 6-8

Ingredients:

4 oz (110 g) chicken livers
1 small can water chestnuts – cut in half

½ lb (225 g) smoked streaky bacon
8 tablesp. rich soya sauce

Method

1.   Cut the livers into bite sized pieces and marinate in 4 tablesp. of soya sauce.

2.   Marinate the water chestnuts in the remaining 4 tablesp. of soya sauce and leave both the livers and chestnuts in the fridge for 2 hours.

3.   Wrap a piece of the liver and a chestnut half in a rasher of bacon (rather messy, but do persevere). Hold together with *wooden* toothpicks.

4.   Place under the grill and cook slowly turning once until the bacon is crisp.

Serve on warmed plate before a meal or as an evening treat.

14. *Leek and Watercress Soup*

Serves 4

Ingredients:

1 lb leeks (450 g) – washed, trimmed and sliced
2 bunches watercress – keep a few sprigs back for garnishing
¼ pt (150 ml) single cream or top of the milk

1 large potato – peeled and diced
1½ pt (850 ml) stock made with marmite and water*
2 tablesp. vegetable oil
pinch of black pepper
*1½ teasp. marmite to
1½ pt (850 ml) of water

Method

1.   Heat the oil in a large heavy saucepan.

2.   Add the leeks, watercress, potato and black pepper.

48

3. Cover and on a very low heat allow the ingredients to sweat for 15 minutes. Stir occasionally.

4. Add the stock and simmer for a further 15 minutes.

5. Cool slightly and then liquidise.

6. *To serve:* Reheat to boiling point. Take off the heat and stir in the cream. Do not reboil otherwise it will curdle.

Garnish with sprigs of watercress.

15. *Mixed Liver Pâté*

It is quick and delicious pâté suitable for all occasions, freezes beautifully – you can double up the quantities if you are having a party.

Serves 4-6

Ingredients:

6 oz (175 g) chicken livers
6 oz (175 g) lamb's liver
6 oz (175 g) smoked bacon – streaky
2 medium sized onions

2 cloves of garlic
4 tablesp. milk (top of the milk)
1 tablesp. fresh parsely – chopped

Method

1. Chop the bacon and livers.

2. Peel and slice the onions.

3. Place the onions, livers, bacon and garlic in the frying pan and cook very slowly until tender for about 20 minutes. A frying pan with a lid is ideal as the steam cooks the food without it becoming brown.

4. Cool. Liquidise, adding the top of the milk to provide enough liquid for the liquidiser to work. Process for between 2-4 minutes.

5. Turn into a ¾ pint (425 ml) terrine. Sprinkle the chopped fresh parsely over the surface and chill.

Serve with crackers or wholemeal bread. This dish is rich in iron and protein and is therefore a very good addition to a pregnancy diet.

16. *Broccoli Soup*

Broccoli is very low in calories, but rich in a variety of mineral salts, which make it an excellent addition to a well balanced and healthy diet. Coupled with the other ingredients this makes a delicious and nourishing soup for any occasion.

Ingredients:

10 oz (275 g) frozen broccoli
¾ pint (425 ml) milk
4 fl oz (110 ml) single cream
1 medium onion – peeled and
  roughly chopped

2 teasp. marmite
pinch of salt
dash of ground nutmeg
chopped chives to garnish

Method

1. Place the thawed broccoli, chopped onion and ¼ pint (150 ml) of the milk in a food processor or liquidiser. Blend until smooth.

2. Add all the remaining ingredients and blend for a further 5-10 seconds.

3. Chill thoroughly and serve sprinkled with chopped chives.

If you do not like cold soups you can heat this gently but do not boil otherwise the cream will curdle.

MAIN DISHES

The main dish of a meal should be meat based and served with vegetable or a salad to make it complete. You should have one main dish daily to ensure you obtain sufficient nutrients, remembering to have liver once a week.

MAIN DISH RECIPES

17. *Thatched Fish and Mango Pie*

Fish is a very useful protein food. White fish has a low fat content which makes it easy to digest and is lower in calories than most other protein foods.

Serves 4

Ingredients:
1-1¼ lb (450-560 g) white fish
  e.g. cod, coley, haddock
1½-2 lbs (675-900 g) old potatoes,
  boiled and creamed
1 egg, size 3
2 tablesp. mayonnaise

4 oz (110 g) cheese (Cheddar) –
  grated
4 oz (110 g) wholemeal breadcrumbs
2 heaped tablesp. mango chutney

1-2 pint (570 ml - 1.1 litre) ovenproof
  serving bowl

Method
1. To cook the fish – simply place in a saucepan and cover with cold water. Bring to the boil and simmer for 15 minutes, drain and allow to cool.

2. Skin the fish and flake using a fork. Put on one side.

3. Take the creamed potatoes and beat in the egg and mayonnaise and then stir in the fish.

4.   Place the mixture in the oven proof serving bowl. Then top with the 2 heaped tablesp. of mango chutney.

5.   Sprinkle half the breadcrumbs on top and then all the cheese and finally the remaining breadcrumbs.

6.   Bake for 20-25 minutes at Gas Mark 3, 325°F, 170°C, until bubbling and golden brown.

Serve with broccoli spears or a mixed green salad.

---

18. *Apple and Tuna Toss*

Fish such as tuna, sardines and tinned mackerel contain small soft bones which are rich in calcium, which together with vitamin D is necessary for the growth and development of bones and teeth.

Serves 1-2

Ingredients:

1 head of lettuce (iceberg type) – shredded
1 red apple – cored and chopped
1 green apple – cored and chopped
one small tin mandarin oranges in natural juice – drained
one 7¼ oz (220 g) tin tuna fish
2 oz (50 g) chopped walnuts (optional)

Dressing:
3-4 tablesp. mayonnaise
2 teasp. soya sauce
1 teasp. lemon juice

Method

1.   Combine the lettuce, apples, mandarin oranges, tuna fish and walnuts in a salad bowl.

2.   Combine the mayonnaise, soya sauce and lemon juice and toss well until all the ingredients are coated.

3.   Chill.

Serve as a midday meal with a wholemeal roll and fresh fruit to follow.

19. *Scampi Provençale*

Serves 4

Ingredients:

1 lb (450 g) fresh or frozen scampi
3 fresh plump tomatoes
1 small onion – finely chopped
1 clove of garlic – crushed
1 tablesp. vegetable oil

1 tablesp. fresh parsley
dash of wine vinegar
finely ground black pepper
lemon slices
sprigs of parsley

Method

1.   Heat the oil in a frying pan and sauté the onion and garlic.

2.   Add the tomatoes, scampi and chopped parsely.

3.   Add the wine vinegar to moisten.

4.   Cook for 4-5 minutes. Season to taste.

5.   Serve immediately on warmed plates with lemon slices and sprigs of parsley.

Serve with jacket potatoes and freshly boiled carrots and french beans.

This is a delicious meal and would grace any dinner party.

20. *Tuna Surprise*

Serves 2-3

Ingredients:

one 7½ (210 g) can tuna – drained
     and flaked
6 oz (175 g) short grain rice –
     cooked
2-3 oz (50-75 g) frozen peas –
     cooked and drained

3 oz (75 g) cheddar cheese – grated
1 egg
¼ pint (150 ml) milk
tomato wedges to garnish
a 1-2 pint (570 ml-1.1 litre)
     ovenproof dish

Method

1.   Mix the tuna, brown rice and peas together in large bowl.

2.   Place in the ovenproof dish and press down using the back of a fork.

3.   Beat the egg in a bowl and add the milk and cheese.

4.   Pour over the rice mixture.

5.   Bake for 30-35 minutes at Gas Mark 5, 375°F, 190°C until golden brown.

6.   Garnish with tomato wedges.

Excellent as a quick lunch time dish with either salad or slices of wholemeal bread.

21. *Oven Baked Scampi*

A quick nutritious meal which is delicious served with jacket potatoes and a mixed salad.

Serves 4

Ingredients:

1 oz (25 g) butter
3 tablesp. soya oil
1 clove of garlic – crushed
pinch of salt
a dash of cayenne pepper

2 tablesp. lemon juice
4 spring onions – peeled and
   chopped
1 lb frozen, peeled scampi

Method

1.   Place all the ingredients (except the scampi) in a frying pan and heat gently, stirring all the time, for 2-3 minutes.

2.   Add the scampi and mix well.

3.   Transfer to an ovenproof serving dish and bake for 10 minutes at Gas Mark 6, 400°F, 200°C.

Garnish with watercress and lemon wedges and triangles of toasted wholemeal bread.

22. *Fish and Cheese Bake*

One ounce (25 g) of cheese provides as much calcium as one-third of a pint of milk. Calcium requirements are greatly increased during pregnancy as baby's bone and teeth development has already started.

Eat more cheese and other milk products if you do not like drinking milk.

Serves 4

Ingredients:
Base:

1 lb (450 g) fish (white) – types suitable are cod, coley, hake
½ pt (275 ml) milk
½ oz (10 g) margarine
½ oz (10 g) flour
2 oz (50 g) mushrooms – washed and chopped

1 tablesp. chopped fresh parsley *or* a pinch of dried parsley
pinch each of salt and pepper

Topping:
4 oz (110 g) breadcrumbs
2 oz (50 g) cheddar cheese – grated

Method

1. Cook the fish, remove the skin and flake: you can either steam the fish on a plate over a saucepan of water or simmer it in the ½ pint (275 ml) of milk until tender, making sure you retain the milk to prepare the later sauce, topping up if necessary. If you have a micro-wave oven cook in a suitable dish using the required amount of milk from the ½ pint (275 ml) milk as indicated by your instruction book.

2. Prepare the sauce by melting the margarine and stirring in the flour. Then slowly stir in the milk, making sure you stir well to remove any lumps. Return to the heat and bring slowly to the boil, stirring all the time.

3. Stir in the chopped mushrooms, salt and pepper, and chopped fresh parsely. If you are going to use dried parsely add only a pinch otherwise its taste will be too overpowering.

4. Taste the sauce and alter the seasoning if necessary. Stir in the flaked fish and mix well. Then transfer to a 2-2½ pint (1.1-1.4 litre) oven/micro-wave proof dish. Allow to cool.

5. *To make the topping:* place the breadcrumbs and cheese in a bowl. Stir well, and sprinkle over the fish base.

This dish can then be eaten straight away by placing in a moderate oven, Gas Mark 4, 350°F, 180°C, for 30-35 minutes until thoroughly warmed and then served with a selection of fresh vegetables or cooled and then frozen for up to 3 months, to provide a very useful standby meal. If you have a micro-waven oven it could be defrosted and reheated in minutes. Served from a micro-wave use wholemeal bread to give improved colour to the completed dish.

N.B. You could make several of these at one time and store them in your freezer to use on those occasions when you're too tired to make anything else or haven't a clue as to what to serve for tea.

23. *Shrimp Salad*

This is a delicious lunchtime dish that is a treat in itself, especially if you have time to invite a friend round to enjoy it with you. It is a meal rich in protein and contains a good assortment of those essential nutrients needed to provide the building bricks of a new life. It is, at the same time, relatively low in calories so you will not put on unwanted extra pounds.

Ingredients:
Salad:
4-6 oz (110-175 g) cooked and peeled shrimps

1 small avocado pear – peeled and sliced

6-8 leaves of lettuce or shredded red cabbage

2 oz (50 g) stuffed green olives with pimentos (sweet red peppers) – sliced

a quarter of a cucumber – peeled and sliced

Dressing:
4 oz (110 g) cottage cheese
1 hard boiled **egg – quartered**
3-4 tablesp. tomato juice
¼ teasp. french mustard

Method
To prepare the dressing – this can be made in advance:

1.   Combine the cottage cheese, egg, tomato juice and mustard in a liquidiser. Blend until smooth.

2.   Cover and chill until the salad is to be served.

To prepare the salad:

1.   Mix together the shrimps, avocado, cucumber, olives and lettuce (or shredded red cabbage) in a medium-sized salad bowl.

2.   Toss gently – pour over the prepared dressing and toss again, until well mixed.

Serve straightaway with warmed wholemeal rolls for an excellent lunch-time meal.

24. *Lemon Baked Chicken*

Body tissue is itself protein. We must therefore eat protein foods for growth of tissue (in the case of children and for repair of damaged tissue in children and adults). Chicken is a good source of such protein, but poor in folic acid so should not be eaten as a main protein food. (Red meats are rich in folic acid, and are an essential part of a pre-conception and pregnancy eating programme.)

Serves 4

Ingredients:

4 chicken portions (preferably breast)	pinch each of salt and black pepper
	1 tablesp. fresh thyme
2 oz (50 g) melted butter	1 lemon unpeeled and thinly sliced

Method

1. Place the chicken portions in a buttered roasting tin.

2. Pour over the melted butter.

3. Sprinkle with the salt, pepper and chopped fresh thyme.

4. Arrange the lemon slices on top of the chicken portions. Cover with foil and bake for 45 minutes at Gas Mark 4, 350°F, 180°C.

5. Remove the foil and bake for a further 15-20 minutes until golden brown.

Serve with jacket potatoes and a selection of vegetables.

---

25. *Malfate Caruso*

Serves 4-6

Ingredients:

large tin of tomatoes	2 medium sized onions
1 clove of garlic	a pinch each of salt and pepper
a good pinch each of oregano and basil	a squeeze of lemon juice
	2 tablespoons soya oil
8 oz (225 g) chopped chicken livers	Pasta shapes to serve – quantity according to appetite

Method

1. Slice the onions and fry gently in the oil.

2. Add the tomatoes, garlic and all the seasoning. Simmer for 20 minutes.

3. Add the lemon juice.

4.   In a separate frying pan sauté the chicken livers in a tablesp. of oil for 5 minutes.

5.   Add to the tomato mixture and cook for a further 3 minutes.

To serve: Pour the meat sauce over a bed of freshly boiled pasta shapes: preferably wholemeal pasta to get those **extra nutrients**.

26. *Hot Curried Fruit*

This is an absolutely delicious accompaniment to gammon or roast pork. It provides a change from the traditional apple sauce and is very simple to prepre.

Serves 8

Ingredients:

8 oz (225 g) raw cane sugar
pinch of salt
1 teaspoon mild curry powder
3 oz (75 g) vegetable margarine
2 lbs (900 g) fruit made up of a

combination of pineapple, pears, peaches, apricots or mandarin oranges
1-2 oz (25-50 g) cherries – to give extra colour

Method

1.   Combine the sugar, salt, curry powder and vegetable margarine in a suacepan and bring slowly to the boil.

2.   Reduce the heat and simmer for 2 minutes.

3.   Place the fruit in an oven-proof dish and pour over the prepared sauce.

4.   Bake for 20 minutes at Gas Mark 2, 300°F, 150°C.

Serve in a separate bowl so that each person can help him/her self.

Serve hot but not boiling.

This accompaniment is quite rich, and is therefore high in calories, so only have on very special occasions.

27. *Quick Veal Meatballs in Tomato Sauce*

Serves 3-4

Ingredients:

12 oz (350 g) minced veal
1 tablesp. cornflour
pinch of salt
one 15 oz (425 g) can tomatoes

pinch of sweet basil
pinch of oregano
a cast iron casserole is ideal for this dish

Method

1.   Place the tomatoes, the herbs and salt in the casserole and mash using a fork. Bring slowly to the boil.

2.   Divide the veal into 12 balls, ensuring that they are of even size, otherwise they will not cook evenly. Dust your hands with the cornflour to prevent the meat sticking to them and roll the balls in the remaining cornflour giving them all an even coating.

3.   Drop the prepared meat balls into the simmering liquid and simmer for 5 minutes.

4.   Place the casserole in a preheated oven at Gas Mark 3, 325°F, 170°C, for a further 35-40 minutes.

5.   The cornflour will thicken the liquid and the meat balls should be removed very gently to prevent them from breaking up.

6.   Serve on a bed of brown rice and add a selection of green **vegetables** to make a complete meal.

28. *Indonesian Kebabs (Saté)*

All foods contain calories. Protein as found in meat is primarily required for tissue growth and repair. If insufficient carbohydrate (starchy) foods are eaten to provide energy, protein may be used for energy rather than for its main function. This is called the protein sparing action of carbohydrates. It is therefore important to include some carbohydrates foods in your diet even if you are slimming.

This dish is to be made the day *BEFORE*

Serves 6-8

Ingredients:

1½ lbs (675 g) pork tenderloin
1 oz (25 g) butter
1 tablesp. lemon juice plus the rind
½ teasp. tabasco sauce
1 small onion – grated
3 teasp. raw cane sugar
1 teasp. coriander
½ teasp. ground cumin

½ teasp. ginger
1 clove of garlic – crushed
6 tablesp. Indonesian soya sauce
  (this is a thick heavy soya sauce,
  slightly sweet in taste)
small pinch each of salt and black
  pepper
8 skewers

Method

1. Cut the pork into ½" (1 cm) cubes. Place in a medium sized shallow dish.

2. Melt the butter and add *all* the remaining ingredients.

3. Bring slowly to the boil and simmer gently for 5 minutes.

4. Pour sauce over the meat and cover with foil. Leave in the fridge overnight.

5. Turn the meat occasionally and do not worry if the butter congeals.

6. *To cook*: Place the meat on the skewers and reserve the liquor. Barbecue or grill for 15-20 minutes, turning several times.

7. Meanwhile reheat the marinade and serve separately to pour over the kebabs.

8. *To serve:* Place the kebabs on a bed of rice and serve with a mixed salad taken from the vegetable section of the book (see Pages 89-101).

---

29. *Fandango*

Like all red meat, beef is a good source of iron. Iron is particularly important for expectant mothers as they develop a greater blood volume, and are therefore more susceptible to anaemia.

A quick and economical dish that is excellent as a mid-week meal and very nutritious into the bargain.

Serves 6

Ingredients:

1 lb (450 g) minced beef
1 medium sized onion – chopped
8 oz (225 g) mushrooms – washed
   and quartered
2 teasp. oregano
1-2 cloves of garlic – crushed
one 10 oz (275 g) packet frozen
   spinach – thawed and drained

OR 10 oz (275 g) fresh spinach –
   washed and shredded and
   sautéed in 1 tablesp. vegetable oil
2 sticks celery – washed and diced
8 oz (225 g) natural yoghurt
4 tablesp. cooked brown rice
a good pinch of black pepper
6 oz (175 g) cheddar cheese – grated

Method

1.   Brown the mince in a non-stick frying pan for 2 minutes. Then add the onions, mushrooms, garlic and oregano. Stir-fry for a further 2 minutes.

2.   Stir in the spinach, natural yoghurt, rice and pepper. Heat through, stirring gently.

3.   Turn into an ovenproof dish and top with the grated cheese.

4.   Bake at Gas Mark 4, 350°F, 180°C for 40 minutes.

This is a complete meal in itself and could be made before and simply reheated in a micro-wave oven. It isn't really suitable for freezing.

---

30. *Beef with Red Kidney Beans*

Serves 4

Ingredients:

¾ lbs (350 g) minced beef
4 oz (110 g) chicken livers –
   liquidised or finely chopped
1 red pepper
1 green pepper
washed, trimmed and sliced
1 14 oz (400 g) can red kidney
   beans – drained and rinsed

1 tablesp. vegetable oil
1 clove of garlic – crushed
1 teasp. cayenne pepper
4-6 tablesp. tomato puré
pinch of salt
7-10 fl oz (200-275ml) water or
   stock

Method

1.   Heat the oil in a heavy saucepan, add the minced beef and garlic and stir until the meat changes colour.

2.   Add the cayenne pepper, salt and liquidised or finely chopped chicken livers. Continue frying for a further 2 minutes.

3.   Add the chopped peppers, tomato purée and the liquid and simmer for 45 minutes.

4.   Add the drained and rinsed red kidney beans and mix carefully so as not to break up the beans. Continue cooking for a further 10 minutes.

5.   Serve hot on a bed of freshly boiled rice with a side salad of lettuce, tomatoes, cucumber and spring onions.

Excellent as an economical dish to serve at a dinner party.

31. *Sweet and Sour Chili Ribs*

The aroma from the ribs will start anyone's mouth watering!

Ingredients:

2 lbs pork spare ribs (ask your butcher or supermarket to cut your ribs)
4 oz (110 g) Muscovado sugar
3 tablesp. tomato sauce (without colour or preservatives)

3 tablesp. vinegar
1 tablesp. Worcester sauce
½ teasp. chili powder
4 tablesp. water
1 onion – diced

Method

1.   Remove any excess fat from the ribs and place in an open roasting tin.

2.   Place all the other ingredients in a mixing bowl and mix well.

3.   Pour over the ribs and bake uncovered at Gas Mark 1, 275°F, 140°C (or at the lowest possible setting) for 2-2½ hours. Turn and baste during cooking.

This is an excellent dish to put in the oven in the morning. Using the oven timer to ensure it is ready when required will enable you to get on with any outstanding work or chores.

32. *Chinese Beef*

Those proteins found in meat are made up of constituents called amino acids. Animal protein contains all the essential amino acids (defined as those amino acids which the body cannot make and must therefore eat). Vegetable protein has one or more amino acids missing and so a combination of vegetables must be eaten to provide all the essential amino acids.

Serves 2

Ingredients:

8-10 oz (225-275g) steak e.g. sirloin, frysteak, tenderised steak – the better the quality obviously the more palatable the dish

1 small onion

1 clove of garlic

1 large red pepper

1 large green pepper

2 tablesp. peanut oil

2 tablesp. soya sauce

2 teasp. cornflour mixed to a smooth paste with a little water

pinch of salt

Method

1. Prepare the meat, peppers and onions by cutting into thin strips using a sharp knife. Put into a bowl, keeping the meat separate, and put to one side.

2. Heat the peanut oil in a large frying pan and add the garlic. Fry for one minute.

3. Add the meat and continue cooking for 2 minutes, or until the meat has changed colour.

4. Add the peppers and onions and cook for a further 1-3 minutes.

5. Add the soya sauce and salt and stir well.

6. Add the cornflour and water. Mix and cook until all the ingredients are coated with the cornflour mixture.

Serve immediately either with brown rice or beansprout salad (*see* Page 81).

---

33. *Liver Persian Style*

Serves 4

Ingredients:

1 lb (450 g) lamb's liver	pinch of salt – optional
1 large leek – shredded	8 oz (225 g) basmati rice
1 lb (450 g) fresh tomatoes	½ lb fresh spinach (225 g)
2 tablesp. soya oil	1 clove of garlic – crushed
2 teasp. dill seeds	1 oz (25 g) butter
pinch of black pepper	1 oz (25 g) flaked almonds

Method

1. Wash and trim the liver using a pair of sharp kitchen scissors and cut the meat into thin 2″ (5 cm) strips.

2. Heat the oil in a heavy casserole and add the garlic, pepper, salt and dill seeds. Fry quite vigorously for 1 minute to release all the delicious flavours from the herbs and spices.

3. Turn down the heat, and add the meat and shredded leek and stir fry for 5 minutes until the meat is sealed.

4. Wash the tomatoes and cut into quarters and place in the casserole. Cover, bring back up to simmering point.

5. Transfer to a preheated oven at Gas Mark 3, 325°F, 170°C, and cook for 1-1½ hours until the meat is tender.

N.B. Remove the lid towards the end of the cooking time to reduce the quantity of liquid as you need only leave enough to keep the meat moist.

To serve: Boil the basmati rice in ample water until tender and drain well. Place on an oval serving plate and keep warm. Then wash and trim the spinach and shred it very finely.

Melt the butter in a frying pan and fry the garlic. Then add the spinach and sauté until tender. Place this down the centre of the rice and sprinkle on the flaked almonds.

Serve the two dishes together to create a very exotic dish: a dish rich in vital nutrients which I always serve to people who say they loathe liver and one which is invariably enjoyed. I first became acquainted with it in Iran a number of years ago!

A good recipe to tempt those who are not keen on offal. Liver is the most concentrated source of iron, which is vital for preventing anaemia.

---

34. *Foie eminçé à la sauge* (*Sliced liver with fresh sage*) ⟻

A traditional french recipe to serve calf's liver at its best.

Serves 2

Ingredients:

9 oz (250 g) calf's liver – cut into slices

12 large fresh sage leaves – washed and trimmed

2 tablesp. olive oil

1 large clove of garlic – crushed

pinch each of salt and freshly ground black pepper

Method

1. Using a sharp knife cut the liver into thin strips measuring approximately 0.5 cms x 3 cms.

2. Peel the clove of garlic and crush. (Remove the green centre piece as according to a very good French friend of mine this is considered to be indigestible and especially if you are pregnant you do not want it repeating on you.)

3. Using a non-stick frying pan heat the oil and gently fry the crushed garlic. (Remove the garlic after frying for 1 minute if you dislike a strong garlic flavour).

4. Add the sage leaves and then the slivers of liver.

5. Cook briskly using a high heat for 1 minute. Add the pinches of salt and freshly ground pepper and cook for a further 2 minutes until tender.

To add a little *je ne sais quoi*, add a good pinch of cayenne pepper to the oil.

Serve immediately with a selection of freshly cooked vegetables and some good company.

35. *Sausage Chili*

Serves 4

Ingredients:

½ lb (225 g) minced beef or ground beef – ground beef has less fat and is becoming more readily available in supermarkets

½ lb (225 g) thick plump sausages (nitrate free if possible*) – sliced

1 medium onion – chopped

1 medium green pepper – chopped

3 sticks celery – chopped

1 15 oz (425 g) tin of red kidney beans

1 15 oz (425 g) tin of tomatoes

4 tablesp. tomato purée

1 clove garlic – crushed

1 teasp chili powder

1 pinch of salt and ground black pepper

1 tablesp. of vegetable oil

Method

1. Heat the oil and sauté the minced beef, garlic, chili powder and sliced sausages for 4-5 minutes in a large heavy casserole.

2. Add the onions, green pepper and celery and stir.

3. Stir in the tinned tomatoes, tomato purée, salt and black pepper.

4. Place in a moderately hot oven for 1 hour.

5. Add the drained and rinsed kidney beans and return to the oven for a further 20 minutes.

Serve with any salad dish described in this book together with brown rice and you will provide your family with a nutritious and economical meal.

* Nitrates are added to sausages and other meat products as preservatives. If you ask your butcher he may be able to make you up a batch of sausages without the chemical preservatives.

36. *Florentine meat loaf*

Serves 4

Ingredients:

1 lb (450 g) ground or minced beef
6 oz (175 g) wholemeal bread
   crumbs
5 oz (150 g) frozen spinach –
   defrosted and drained
1 egg, size 2, beaten

2 tablesp. milk or cream
1 tablesp. soya sauce
2 tablesp. tomato purée
pinch of salt and ground black
   pepper

Method

1.   Combine the egg, milk, breadcrumbs, spinach, soya sauce, salt, black pepper and tomato purée.

2.   Add the beef and mix well.

3.   Line a 2 lb (900 g) loaf tin with foil and press the mixture into the tin.

4.   Bake at Gas Mark 4, 350°F, 180°C for 50-60 minutes or until golden brown.

5.   Remove from the tin and serve on a warm plate with potatoes and the vegetable of your choice.

37. *Pot Roast Beef with Horseradish à la Maison*

Serves 6 or more

Ingredients:

one piece of boned and rolled
   brisket (large enough to feed
   your family or guests – allow 4-6
   oz (110-175 g) per person –
   minimum weight 1½ lbs (675 g)
8 shallot onions
½ lb (225 g) carrots – cut into strips
   4″ (10 cms) in length
1 small swede cut into strips 4″ (10
   cms) in length

2 cloves of garlic – crushed
pinch of black pepper
4 tablesp tomato purée
½ pint (275 ml) stock or water
1 tablesp. soya oil
2 bay leaves
pinch of basil
sprig of thyme
(a large casserole – le creuset
   gives the best results)

Method

1. Wipe and trim the meat.

2. Place the oil in a heavy casserole and heat for one minute. Add the garlic, basil, thyme and black pepper. Stir – this helps bring out the flavour of the herbs.

3. Add the joint of brisket and cook on each side for 5 minutes on a moderate heat. This is to seal the meat and not to actually cook it.

4. Add the prepared shallots, swede and carrots.

5. Add the tomato purée and stock and stir until well mixed.

6. Cover and bring to simmering point.

7. Place in a moderate oven at Gas Mark 3, 170°C, 325°F and cook for 2½ hours.

To serve: Slice the joint and arrange down the centre of warm, oval plate. Arrange the vegetables around it. Strain the liquor to remove the fat and pour over the meat.

Serve with freshly boiled potatoes and Horseradish à la maison.

Horseradish à la Maison

Serves 6

Ingredients:

6 tablesp. mayonnaise	1 large dill cucumber – finely
2 teasp. very finely grated fresh	chopped
horseradish	1 tablesp. capers – cut into quarters

Method

1. Combine all the ingredients together. Chill and serve with the beef.

N.B. This can be made in advance which will allow time for the flavours to mingle.

38. *Spiced Liver with Orange*

Serves 4

Ingredients:

1 lb (450 g) lamb's liver – sliced and coated in seasoned flour
1 oz (25 g) wholewheat flour
1 onion – chopped
2 oranges
1 clove of garlic – crushed
1 teasp. fresh thyme
one 10¼ oz (283 g) can prepared mild curry mix e.g. roghan gosht, korma – use authentic varieties only
1 oz (25 g) butter

Method

1. Fry the liver in a little butter and place in an ovenproof casserole. (Keep in a warm place.)

2. Fry the onion and garlic for 2-3 minutes. Add the thyme, curry mix and grated rind and juice of one orange.

3. Heat and pour over the liver.

4. Bake for 15-20 minutes for flavours to mingle at Gas Mark 2, 300°F, 150°C.

To serve: Garnish with slices of the orange and freshly boiled brown rice.

VEGETARIAN RECIPES

Being a vegetarian is a personal matter, but becoming pregnant will also mean that you should alter your diet to accommodate your baby's needs. Generally speaking, when the mother has been making sound food choices, all she needs to do is to increase the amount of foods she is eating to make sure she is meeting her increased nutrient requirements.

If you are a vegan you will need to ensure that you are having sufficient iron and Vitamin C in your diet. One way of doing this is to cook in cast iron cook ware.

However, if you have not eaten animal products for a long time I suggest you discuss your new diet requirements with your doctor.

VEGETARIAN RECIPES

39. *Felafel (Patties)*

This is a middle eastern dish. This dish does not have to be eaten at any particular time of the day – they can be served as appetisers or with a salad to provide the main dish. I first tasted them when I visited Iran several years ago. At home we used to like to make them on wet Saturday afternoons to cheer us up!

Ingredients:

½ lb (225 g) chick peas
4 tablesp. fresh parsley
1 tablesp. fresh coriander
pinch of cayenne pepper
two cloves of garlic – crushed
1 bunch finely chopped spring
   onions

1 teasp. ground cumin
¼-½ teasp. baking powder
pinch of saffron for colour but
   turmeric will do

Method

1. Soak the chick peas overnight and then cook until tender. This will take 2-3 hours and several top-ups of water in an ordinary saucepan so I would recommend you cook them in a pressure coooker at 15 lbs pressure for 45 minutes.

2. Drain the peas and mash or make into a smooth consistency in a blender or food processor. A little of the cooking liquid may be needed to help give a smooth consistency.

3. Place in a mixing bowl and add the onions, garlic, chopped fresh parsely, coriander, cumin, cayenne pepper, turmeric and baking powder. (A pinch of saffron may be used instead of turmeric.) Mix well.

4. Take walnut sized lumps and make into flat cakes 1½″ (4 cm) in diameter.

5. Place in the fridge for 30 minutes.

6. Deep fat fry until dark and golden. Drain on absorbent paper.

Yummie!

40. *Tofu Coleslaw*

Serves 8-10

Ingredients:

1 10 oz (275 g) pack silken tofu
half a firm white cabbage
1 medium sized cooking apple
1 medium sized onion
2 medium sized carrots
2 dill pickles – finely chopped

1 tablesp. capers
2 tablesp. toasted sesame seeds
2 oz (50 g) raisins
2 oz (50 g) roasted cashew nuts
1 clove of garlic – peeled and halved

Method

1.   Drain the liquid from the tofu and beat with a fork in a large mixing bowl. Add chopped dill pickles and capers. Put to one side.

2.   Wash and trim the vegetables and then finely chop them. This can be done in a food processor. The apple, onion and carrot may be grated.

3.   Add to the tofu together with the raisins and cashew nuts. Mix well.

4.   Turn into a serving bowl which has been rubbed with the garlic.

5.   Sprinkle with the toasted sesame seeds just before serving so that they keep their crunchiness.

This may be served as a side salad to a main dish or as a quick meal served with wholemeal bread. The latter will provide a balance of nutrients and fibre. It does, however, lack the important B vitamins so perhaps marmite or misco on your bread will rectify this deficiency.

41. *Vegetable Pizza*

Serves 1-2

Ingredients:
Base:
6 oz (175 g) wholemeal flour plus
    1½ teasp. baking powder
1 oz (25 g) vegetable margarine
enough natural yoghurt to mix to a
    firm, but soft dough

Topping:
1 small tin tomatoes
1 small onion – chopped
1 courgette – washed and diced
1 large carrot – grated
1 small red pepper – diced
seasoning of your own choice

Method

1. Place the flour and baking powder in a mixing bowl and rub in the vegetable margarine.

2. Mix to a firm but soft dough with the natural yoghurt.

3. Knead gently and roll out into a square ¼" (5 mm) in depth. Place on a floured baking sheet.

4. Top first with the tomatoes followed by the onion, courgette, red pepper and finally the grated carrot.

5. Sprinkle with herbs of your own choice – I enjoy fresh parsley and thyme.

6. Bake for 30-40 minutes at Gas Mark 4, 350°F, 180°C.

Serve hot with a salad of your choice.

42. *Mixed Vegetable Pilaf with Roasted Almonds*

Serves 4

Ingredients:

4 oz (110 g) flaked almonds
4 tablesp. soya oil
1 medium onion – peeled and diced
8 oz (225 g) long grain brown rice
¾ pint water or 1 teasp. marmite and ¾ pint water mixed
½ teasp. turmeric
pinch of salt – optional

4 oz (110 g) celery – diced
4 oz (110 g) french beans cut into 2" (5 cm) pieces
4-6 oz (110-175g) aubergines – cubed
1 small red pepper
3 tomatoes – cut into quarters
1 clove of garlic – crushed

Method

1. Using two tablesp. of the oil fry the almonds, stirring constantly until they are brown. Place on absorbent kitchen paper and put to one side.

2. Heat the remaining 2 tablesp. of oil in a heavy saucepan and add the onion and garlic. Fry until soft but not brown.

3. Add the rice, water, turmeric and salt and bring to the boil. Cover. Simmer until the rice is cooked, for about 35–45 minutes.

4. In a small amount of water cook the celery, french beans, aubergines and red pepper until just tender.

5. Combine the vegetables, rice and half of the almonds in a large

bowl. Transfer to a warmed serving bowl. Sprinkle on the remaining almonds as garnish.

Serve with wholemeal bread rolls and a little butter.

---

43. *Broccoli Casserole*

Serves 4-5

Ingredients:

1 clove garlic – crushed
1 medium onion – chopped
1 oz (25 g) butter
1 lb fresh broccoli – cut into bite sized pieces
10 oz (275 g) natural yoghurt
7 oz (200 g) mature cheddar cheese – grated

4 oz (110 g) button mushrooms – washed
4 oz (110 g) flaked almonds
4 oz (110 g) wholemeal breadcrumbs

Method

1. Sauté the onion, garlic and button mushrooms in the butter.

2. Place in a medium sized casserole.

3. Parboil the broccoli (cook 4-6 minutes until still crunchy). Add to the casserole along with 2 oz (50 g) of the almonds.

4. Using a separate bowl mix together the yoghurt and cheese.

5. Mix into the casserole carefully.

6. Top with the almonds and breadcrumbs and bake at 350°F, 180°C, Gas Mark 4 for 35-40 minutes.

This is a very nutritious dish for a lacto-vegetarian as it contains ample protein from the cheese, almonds and yoghurt; and folic acid in the broccoli. This should always be included in your weekly menus.

---

44. *Tofu and Spinach Quiche*

Serves 6

Ingredients:

Using a 10″ (25 cm) flan dish
Pastry
8 oz (225 g) wholewheat flour
1 oz (25 g) soya flour
4 oz (110 g) vegetable fat
enough cold water to make a firm
    dough
(1 teasp. of cold water to every
    ounce (25 g) of flour)

Fillings
10 oz (275 g) tofu
8 oz (225 g) fresh or frozen spinach
4 oz (110 g) mild cheese e.g.
    Caerphilly, Lancashire – grated
4 oz (110 g) sweetcorn nibblets
a good pinch of oregano

Method 1 – Using a Food Processor

1. Place the flours in the processor using the twin blade attachment.

2. Roughly chop the fat, and add to the flours.

3. Process for 4-5 seconds.

4. Add the liquid – one teasp. of cold water to every ounce (25 g) of flour. I find that adding an ice-cube to the water gives a better pastry. I also always add an extra two teasp. of water for unrefined flour as it seems to soak up the liquid more and the additional water makes it easier to roll out.

5.   Process until the mixture forms several balls, then remove and form into a large ball on a floured surface. This will prevent over processing which can result in a tough pastry. I roll out and line the flan dish and then leave to relax in the fridge (as the pastry can otherwise become difficult to handle).

Method 2 – By Hand
1.   Place the flours in a large mixing bowl.

2.   Cut up the fat into lumps and cover with flour before beginning to rub into the flour.

3.   Rub in until no lumps of fat are left, incorporating as much air as possible.

4.   Add the water, sprinkling it over the surface of the flour.

5.   Mix together with a round-ended knife until a large ball is formed. Draw together using fingertips.

6.   Knead on a floured surface again using the fingertips.

7.   With the pastry line a flan dish and then leave to relax in the fridge.

To prepare the filling:
1.   If using frozen spinach allow to thaw out completely. If using fresh spinach wash and trim and then shred very finely.

2.   Beat the tofu in a bowl until smooth, add the grated cheese, sweetcorn and spinach and mix well until all the ingredients are coated with tofu.

3.   Put all the ingredients in a food processor and blend for 8 seconds for a smoother filling.

4.   Put the prepared filling in the prepared base and sprinkle with oregano. Bake at Gas Mark 4, 350°F, 180°C for 45 minutes until golden brown.

Serve with jacket potatoes or Hash Brownies (*see* page 93).

SPROUTED BEANS

Beans have become more popular as vegetarianism has gained respect, but they can taste rather dull. It is possible, however, to change the dried bean into a crisp and crunchy vegetable by sprouting it, and so open up a whole range of interesting dishes. Sprouted beans contain only 16 calories per 4 oz (110 g) serving and are higher in protein than most other vegetables. The vitamin and mineral content is considerable and they contain virtually no cholestrol.

The most popular sprouted bean is the mung bean, but you can use other beans for a variety of texture and flavour. A good sprout should be clean, white, and very crisp.

How To Prepare Your Own Sprouts

1.   You will need: a large jar such as a coffee jar and an elastic band to fit round the neck OR a kilner jar; J cloth or piece of cheesecloth

2.   You will need 2 oz (50 g) beans for a large kilner jar, as they increase in volume about five times.

3.   Wash and pick over the beans; leave them to soak in water overnight.

4.   Drain the beans; wash again and put them into the jar with the cloth covering the neck and held in place with the elastic band or screw top.

5.   I find the airing cupboard a good place to sprout beans as it gives warmth without light, which would otherwise turn the sprouts green.

6.   Three times a day pour water through the cloth cover, rinse the sprouting beans and drain.

7.   In 3-6 days, depending on the variety, you should have a jar full of sprouts to use.

45. *Beansprout and Carrot Salad*

Serves 4-6 portions

Ingredients:
8 oz (220 g) beansprouts – (mung bean), blanched and chilled
1-2 young carrots, trimmed, cleaned and grated

Dressing:
3 tablesp. soya sauce
2 tablesp. vinegar
1 teasp. sugar
1 teasp. sesame seed oil
(Mix together in a jam jar and shake)

Method
1.   Mix together carrots and bean sprouts.

2.   Pour over the dressing and chill thoroughly.

Excellent with pork dishes.

46. *Chefs Special Soufflé Omelette* (*Alaska Style*)

Serves 1-2

Ingredients:
2 large eggs (size 1)
2 teasp. vegetable oil
4 tablesp. beansprouts, blanched

2 pineapple rings in natural juice, chopped
2 tablesp. ice-cold natural yoghurt.

Method
1. Whisk egg whites until they peak. Fold in the yolks.

2. Heat the oil in a frying pan and use the eggs to make an omelette in the usual way.

3. Over half the omelette, place beansprouts, chopped pineapple and ice cold natural yoghurt.

Fold in half and serve straight away so that the cold yoghurt and hot omelette combine in the mouth like a baked Alaska.

47. *Aduki Sprout Salad*

Serves 4-6

Ingredients:
8 oz (220 g) sprouted aduki beans
6 radishes, chopped
6 oz (170 g) red cabbage, finely
   chopped
2 nectarines, chopped

Dressing:
1 avocado, mashed until smooth
4 tablesp. natural yoghurt
1 tablesp. lemon juice
(Beat until smooth)

Method
1. Blanch aduki sprouts. Chill.

2. Mix all ingredients together.

3. Pour over the dressing and toss.

4. Chill well before serving.

Excellent with Quiche.

48. *Alfalfa Garnish*

Ingredients:
4 tablesp. Alfalfa sprouts
4 tablesp. chopped onion
4 tablesp. chopped parsley

Method
Combine ingredients. Mix together and keep in the fridge and use to garnish any dish – use around the edge of a fish dish or top of a casserole or as a sandwich filling with egg mayonnaise or cottage cheese.

49. *Stir Fry Bean Sprouts*

Serves 4

Ingredients:
8 oz (220 g) sprouted beans – any variety although mung give good results
1-2 tablesp. peanut oil
4 oz (110 g) chopped mushrooms.

1 small red pepper – sliced thinly
1 small green pepper – sliced thinly
4 spring onions, chopped
2 tablesp. soya sauce

Method
1.   Wash and trim the vegetables

2.   Heat the oil in a large frying pan or wok. Add the bean sprouts, mushrooms, peppers and spring onions.

3.   Cook for 2-3 mins., stirring all the time.

4.   Add the soya sauce and continue to cook for a further 1 min.

Serve in a warmed bowl with baked chicken portions or your favourite meat dish.

YOGHURT

A valuable addition to any diet as it has so many valuable qualities.

What is yoghurt?
It is coagulated and fermented milk. This is performed by two safe bacteria called Lactobacillus bulgaricus and Streptococcus thermophilus. Sometimes a third bacteria is used: this is called Lactobacillus acidophilus.

Why so many different natural flavours and consistencies?
It depends on the milk of origin and the method used to make the yoghurt.

Commercial Yoghurt
In Britain yoghurt is generally made from fresh, pasteurized and homogenised cows' milk, and made under carefully controlled temperatures and incubating conditions. Reading the labels shows they are made from milk with varying amounts of butterfat, and often enriched with non-fat milk solids, and stabilized, usually with gelatin. For those wanting to count calories, go for the skimmed milk varieties. Most commercial yoghurt is pasteurized, which lengthens its shelf life, but is useless as a starter as all the live bacteria have been destroyed.

Homemade Yoghurt

The starter or culture that you use can be
1. Homemade yoghurt.
2. Commercial (live) unpasteurized.
3. Dried culture – although expensive can be bought from the health food shop and will keep for several months if kept refrigerated.

To make home-made yoghurt

The Milk:
1. Use fresh whole cows' or goats' milk, U.H.T., sterilized or evaporated milk, adding dried milk up to 2 oz (50 g) per 1 pint (600 ml), which gives a thicker consistency.

2.   If using pasteurized cows's milk or goats' milk, bring to boiling point to kill any remaining bacteria and then allow to cool to blood heat. If using U.H.T., sterilized or evaporated milk, simply bring to blood heat. Test the temperature by dropping a little on your wrist: if it feels comfortable after a slow count to ten then it's fine to use.

3.   Pour heated milk into a container – (e.g. yoghurt makers' thermos flask which has been scalded).

4.   Add starter or culture mix (½ teasp. per pot or 4 teasp. for a flask) and check instructions if using live culture.

5.   Keep in a warm place for up to 8 hours. The airing cupboard is ideal for this job.

You can use home-made once or twice for your next batch, but no more because the bacteria become unstable and break down. There is a bacteria bank in Paris from which British bacteria are obtained, as manufacturers need constant new supplies to ensure that the yoghurt is of a high standard.

The natural yoghurt can then be used in any of the delicious recipes in this book.

Tips on Cooking with Yoghurt

1.   Before heating allow yoghurt to reach room temperature.

2.   Use low cooking temperatures and always add towards the end, otherwise it can curdle.

3.   Folding rather than stirring yoghurt into other ingredients will help keep its original consistency.

4.   For a stiffer consistency, try mixing yoghurt with a beaten egg white.

5.   Yoghurt can often be substituted for milk, cream, buttermilk or sour cream. If replacing milk or cream you may need to use slightly larger quantities of yoghurt. When substituting it for buttermilk, thin to the consistency of buttermilk with a little water. For a consistency similar to sour cream use whole milk yoghurt rather than low-fat yoghurt.

6.   Mix with mayonnaise as a dressing to reduce richness and calories.

7.   Use as a marinade for meat instead of alcohol.

50. *Mushroom and Yoghurt Dip*

Ingredients:

1 tablesp. vegetable oil
4 oz (110 g) mushrooms, finely chopped
4 spring onions, finely chopped
3 oz (75 g) cottage cheese

¼ pt (125 ml) natural yoghurt
salt (optional)
1 tablesp. dill

Method

1.   Gently fry the mushrooms and spring onions in the oil (4 mins)

2.   Beat the cottage cheese in a bowl, add the yoghurt and finally the cooked mushrooms and spring onions.

3.   Add salt if desired.

4.   Place in an attractive bowl and sprinkle on the dill.

Serve with a selection of prepared vegetables as a starter or a dip.

51. *Persian Cheese and Cucumber Starter*

Ingredients:

¾ pt (450 ml) thick set yoghurt
1 cucumber, finely chopped
1 red onion, finely chopped
4 large radishes, grated
6 tablesp. finely chopped walnuts

4 tablesp. washed and dried currants
1 tablesp. fresh dill
1 tablesp. fresh mint
salt (optional)
To serve shredded lettuce

Method

1.   Combine all the ingredients well.

2.   Using an ice-cream scoop, place well-shaped balls of the mixture on to individual plates lined with shredded lettuce.

52. *Lentil Soup*

Serves 4

Ingredients:

6 oz (175 g) brown lentils
1½ pt (900 ml) water or vegetable
   stock
1 tablesp. vegetable oil
1 med. onion, finely chopped

1 med. clove garlic, crushed
½ teasp. cumin
½ teasp. turmeric
salt (optional)
¼ pt (125 ml) natural yoghurt

Method

1.   Place the lentils in a heavy saucepan and add water or stock. Boil for 1-1½ hrs until soft, top up if necessary.

2.   Heat the oil in a frying pan and sauté the onion and garlic.

3.   Add to the lentils with the cumin and turmeric. Simmer for a full 10 mins.

4.   Cool and liquidise to give a smooth consistency.

5.   Return to the saucepan. Heat gently. Do not boil. Add yoghurt and serve.

VEGETABLES
AND
SALADS

Vegetables and salads, especially the dark, leafy ones, play a key role in the pre-conception and pregnancy diet. Use them as much as possible and use as many different fresh vegetables as possible.

VEGETABLES AND SALADS RECIPES

53. *Armenian Spinach Salad*

Unfortunately spinach is not the wonder food it was once claimed to be! Although rich in iron it also contains a substance (oxalic acid) which by combining with the iron renders it unavailable to the body. This means no matter how much you eat you will not derive any benefit from it. Vegetarians frequently eat sufficient foods with a high iron content, but because the iron in vegetables is not as available as that present in animal products they are more susceptible to anaemia.

Serves 4

Ingredients:

1 cucumber – peeled and thinly sliced
¾ lb (350 g) fresh young spinach leaves
1 red onion (if not available spanish will do)
4 oz (110 g) black olives

8 oz (225 g) Feta cheese (Roquefort can also be used)
pinch of freshly ground black pepper
Dressing:
6 tablesp. olive oil
4 tablesp. lemon juice

Method

1.   Wash, trim and dry the spinach and shred.

2.   Place in a salad bowl and combine all the other ingredients and toss.

3.   Place the oil and lemon juice in a clean screw top jam jar and shake vigorously.

4.   Pour over the prepared salad and toss.

54. *Turnip Puff*

Serves 6-8

Ingredients:

2½-3 lbs (1.1-1.35 kg) prepared turnip cut into cubes
2 oz (50 g) butter
2 eggs size 4, beaten
3 tablesp. wholemeal flour
1 tablesp. raw cane sugar

1 teasp. baking powder
pinch each of salt, pepper and nutmeg
4 oz (110 g) wholemeal bread crumbs
2 tablesp. melted butter

Method

1.   Cook the turnip until tender. Drain and mash.

2.   Add the butter and eggs. Beat well using a fork.

3.   Combine the flour, sugar, baking powder, salt, pepper and nutmeg and stir into the mixture using a fork.

4.   Turn into a greased 3 pint (1.65 l) ovenproof dish.

5.   Combine the melted butter and breadcrumbs and sprinkle over the mixture.

6.   Bake for 20-25 minutes at Gas Mark 5, 375°F, 190°C until golden brown.

This dish makes an often plain vegetable into something quite special, and could even be served at a dinner party or with a simple meal of faggots and mashed potatoes.

---

55. *Watercress and Bacon Salad with a Hot Dressing*

A quick and unusual salad to serve with most meals, and very nutritious because watercress is a very good source of calcium and Vitamin C. From a 4 oz (110 g) serving you will receive 222 mg of calcium and 60 mg of Vitamin C which is a good, healthy contribution towards your daily requirements. It may, however, be too ambitious to try and eat 4 oz (110 g) at one sitting so I would suggest you have a watercress based salad most days, or even try it in a soup, but do remember that any cooking will reduce the nutritional value so try, therefore, not to over cook and eat straightaway.

Serves 4-6

Ingredients:

2 bunches watercress	herbs – parsley, sweet basil and
2 tablesp. soya oil	chives
8 rashers smoked, streaky bacon	4-6 oz (110-175 g) button
2 tablesp. cider vinegar	mushrooms - washed and sliced
2 tablesp. of chopped, mixed fresh	pinch each of salt and black pepper

Method

1.   Wash and trim the watercress, shred and place in a salad bowl and chill until required.

2.   Cut up the bacon using scissors and fry in the oil until crisp.

3.   Add the vinegar, herbs, washed and sliced mushrooms and salt and black pepper.

4.   Heat gently for 2-3 minutes, stirring all the time.

5.   Pour over the watercress and toss.

Serve straightway.

Sorrel, spinach or endive can be used to replace the watercress if desired.

---

56. *Hash Brownies*

I was first introduced to this potato dish by an American relative of mine. It provides a welcome change from chips and is very filling and quick to prepare. Brownies can be prepared as individual patties or as a big cake cut into individual portions.

Potatoes are an excellent source of Vitamin C (ascorbic acid) and are beneficial even to those trying to lose weight. Obviously if you eat them in large quantities and with lots of butter or cream they become more fattening. For example 4 oz (100 g) of boiled potatoes provide 80 calories, whilst 4 oz (100 g) of potato made into chips provide approximately 250 calories!

Serves 4-6

Ingredients:

1½ lbs (700 g) potatoes (old preferably)*

1 oz (25 g) butter or vegetable oil

a pinch each of salt and freshly ground black pepper

a little flour for individual patties

Method

1.   Scrub the potatoes clean* – do not remove the skins as the vitamins, especially Vitamin C, lie just below the surface and it's a pity to throw them away.

2.   Either grate the potatoes or use your food processor, using a medium blade.

3.   Once grated remove the excess water by placing the potatoes on absorbent kitchen paper, using several sheets if necessary.

4.   Heat the fat in a frying pan and add the potato. Press down to

93

form a cake, placing a dinner plate over the potato to obtain the correct appearance. Sprinkle with salt and pepper. Recover and cook over a low heat for 15 minutes. Slip a spatula underneath to remove any bits that might be sticking and turn. Cook for a further 10 minutes or until crisp and golden.

5.   For individual brownies simply divide the mixture into 6 equal portions. With floured hands shape into patties and fry on both sides until golden brown.

Serve on a warmed plate to accompany any dish you usually have with potatoes. Also good for barbecues as an alternative to jacket potatoes.

* It would be preferable to use organically grown potatoes as many others on the market have been sprayed and there may be residue of the chemicals used still present in the skins. Ask at your local Organic Gardeners Association for details of suppliers and sources.

---

57. *Parsley Potatoes*

Serves 4-6

Ingredients:

1½-2 lbs (700-900 g) potatoes – this recipe works much better with old potatoes
2 eggs
4 tablesp. vegetable oil (preferably soya)

3 heaped tablesp. chopped fresh parsley
2 cloves garlic – crushed
pinch of salt
pinch of black pepper

Method

1.   Wash and scrub the potatoes and remove any areas that are blemished.

2.   Beat the eggs in a small bowl. Add the oil, garlic, parsley, salt and pepper.

3.   Thinly slice the potatoes; a food processor may be useful for this, especially if you are preparing the dish for several people.

4.   Arrange the potatoes in a shallow oven proof or micro-wave proof dish.

5.   Pour over the egg mixture.

6. Cover with foil if you are going to cook in a conventional oven and bake at Gas Mark 4, 350°F, 180°C, until tender and golden brown. Remove the foil for the last 10 minutes. If cooking in a mirco-wave oven then cover with cling film and cook for 10 minutes on a medium setting. Grill if a brown effect is required.

This dish can be prepared in bulk and frozen. It makes an excellent accompaniment to any meat dish. My family enjoy it with cold meat and salad.

58. *Swiss Cabbage*

An excellent dish to serve with any meal as it contains a wide variety of vegetable so you can be sure of eating lots of nutrients.

Try to eat your vegetables raw or cooked for a minimum length of time. Many vitamins are destroyed by heat or light and if soluble in water are so often thrown out with the cooking liquid – which could be used for soups or gravies.

Serves 6-8

Ingredients:
1 large firm white cabbage – finely shredded
1 small red pepper
1 small green pepper
4 oz (110 g) chopped bacon

2 oz (50 g) vegetable margarine
½ pint (275 ml) stock
1 carrot – chopped
2 sticks celery – chopped
one small onion – chopped
pinch each of salt and pepper

Method
1. Melt the margarine in a heavy saucepan and sauté the onion for 3-4 minutes.

2. Add the peppers, celery, carrot and bacon and cook for a further 3-4 minutes.

3. Add the cabbage and stir well.

4. Add the stock and simmer for 10 – 12 minutes or until the vegetables are just tender.

Take great care not to overcook the cabbage.

---

59. *Crunchy Broccoli Salad*

Serves 5

Ingredients:

¾ lb (350 g) fresh broccoli
1 small cauliflower
3 oz (75 g) lean bacon or ham
2 tablesp. sesame seeds
4 oz (110 g) wholemeal breadcrumbs plus 1 tablesp.
wheatgerm

2 oz (50 g) butter
1 oz (25 g) chopped pecan nuts
pinch of black pepper

Dressing:
2 tablesp. cider vinegar
1 tablesp. vegetable oil

Method

1.   Trim the broccoli and cauliflower and cut into florets.

2.   Blanch in boiling water for 2 minutes. Drain and allow to cool.

3.   Melt the butter in a frying pan. Add the bacon, (or ham), sesame seeds, pecan nuts and wholemeal bread crumbs together with the wheatgerm, and fry until crispy.

4.   Prepare the dressing by simply mixing the cider vinegar and vegetable oil together and then adding the blanched vegetables. Toss well.

5.   Transfer to a serving dish. Sprinkle over the breadcrumbs mixture and a pinch of black pepper.

Serve at room temperature.

---

60. *Green Mayonnaise*

An excellent dressing for any salad and especially good for potato salad

Ingredients:

4 oz (110 g) fresh spinach
2 cloves garlic – crushed
4 tablesp. mayonnaise
pinch each of salt and black pepper
4 fl oz (110 ml) single cream

4 spring onions (include the green
tops)
2 tablesp. olive oil or good quality
salad oil
2 tablesp. cider vinegar

Method
1. Wash and trim the spinach.

2. Roughly chop the spinach and onions and place in a liquidiser or food processor.

3. Add the oil, vinegar and garlic. Blend until smooth.

4. Transfer to a bowl and stir in the mayonnaise, cream and seasoning.

N.B. If too thick then thin down with a little milk to the desired consistency.

This mayonnaise is high in calorie content, so a little and not too often is the answer.

---

61. *Layered Salad*

Serves 4-6

Ingredients:

1 Iceberg lettuce – shredded into bite sized pieces
½ lb (225 g) fresh spinach
5 oz (150 g) petit pois peas – defrosted not cooked

bunch of spring onions – chopped
4 oz (110 g) cooked meat e. g. sliced ham, garlic sausage
3 hard boiled eggs, size 4
5 oz (150 g) mayonnaise

Method
1. Take a glass bowl and layer the ingredients starting with the lettuce followed by the spinach, peas, onions, sliced hard boiled eggs and half of the sliced cooked meat.

2. Completely seal with the mayonnaise and place in the fridge for 2 hours.

3. Sprinkle the remaining sliced ham on top as a garnish.

This is a crisp salad suitable to serve with barbecued foods, gammon, steaks or beefburgers. It is simple but very nutritious.

62. *Greek Spinach Salad*

Serves 4-6

Ingredients:

1 cucumber – thinly sliced
¾ lb (350 g) fresh spinach (young
   leaves only)
1 red onion – thinly sliced
4 oz (110 g) stoned black olives
8 oz (225 g) Feta cheese – cubed

black pepper – freshly ground

Dressing:
4 tablesp. olive oil
2 tablesp. lemon juice

Method

1. Wash and trim the spinach and shred finely. Place in a salad bowl.

2. Combine all the other ingredients and toss.

3. Place the oil and lemon juice in a clean screw-top jam jar and shake well.

4. Pour over the salad and toss. Serve immediately.

This can be served as a starter or as an accompaniment to any meat dish of your choice.

63. *Turnip and Apples*

Serves 6-8

Ingredients:

1 large turnip
1 tablesp. butter
2 large Bramley apples
2 oz (50 g) raw cane sugar
a good pinch of cinammon

Topping:
3 oz (75 g) wholemeal flour
3 oz (75 g) raw cane sugar
2 oz (50 g) butter or vegetable
   margarine

Method

1. Prepare the turnip by peeling, dicing and cooking until tender. Mash until smooth with one tablesp. of butter.

2. Peel and slice the bramley apples and toss in the two ounces (50 g) of sugar and the pinch of cinnamon.

3. Grease a 3 pint (1.65 litre) casserole and arrange the turnip and

apple in layers beginning and ending with the turnip. Put to one side.

4.   Rub the fat into the flour and stir in the sugar.

5.   Place on top of the prepared mixture in the casserole and press down well.

6.   Bake for one hour at Gas Mark 4, 350°F, 180°C.

Serve with a gammon joint, pork chops or pork sausages for a really unusual taste. You will always have requests for this recipe.

---

64. *Wholemeal Pasta Salad*

A good source of fibre. Wholemeal pasta like wholemeal bread is a much more nutritious food than the "white" variety. Although fibre is not strictly a nutrient, as it is not metabolised, it is now recognised as an important dietary component.

Serves 4-6

Ingredients:

6 oz (175 g) wholemeal pasta shapes
2 carrots – peeled and grated
one small tin unsweetened pineapple
   in natural juice – diced
6 oz (175 g) washed beansprouts
1 oz (25 g) alfalfa
half a cucumber – peeled and cubed
6 large Chinese leaves – shredded

Dressing:

2 tablesp. – pineapple juice
2 tablesp. orange juice
6 tablesp. soya oil
2 tablesp. cider vinegar

Method

1.   Cook the pasta in ample water until tender. Drain and place in a large mixing bowl.

2.   Add the grated carrots, diced pineapple, beansprouts, alfalfa and cubed cucumber. Stir.

3.   Prepare the dressing by placing all the ingredients in a clean screwtop jam jar and shaking vigorously.

4.   Pour over the salad and toss.

To serve: shred the Chinese leaves and line a salad bowl with them. Then carefully spoon the prepared salad in the middle and chill for 15-20 minutes.

Serve with cold meat, scotch eggs or perhaps barbecued chicken.

65. *Grapefruit and Avocado Salad*

Serves 4

Ingredients:

2 pink grapefruits
1 large avocado
lemon juice
selection (green) salads, e.g.
   chinese leaves, endive, chicory
2 oz black olives
seeds half pomegranate

Yoghurt Dressing:
½ pt natural yoghurt
2 tablesp. mayonnaise
1 tablesp. lemon juice
1 clove garlic crushed
Mix well together and chill well

Method
1.   Peel and trim the grapefruit.
2.   Halve and slice the avocado. Squirt with lemon juice to stop browning.
3.   Line a bowl with the salad greens, ideally shredded. Place the grapefruit, avocado, olives and pomegranate seeds on top.
4.   Either serve the dressing separately or pour on top.

Serve with other salads or with a main dish.

66. *Apple, Beetroot and Pineapple Salad*

Ingredients:

½ pineapple
8 oz (220 g) cooked beetroot, diced
1 large crisp apple, diced
4 spring onions, chopped
1 tablesp. vegetable oil

1 tablesp. wine vinegar
salt (optional)
¼ pt. (150 ml) natural yoghurt
1 tablesp. chopped parsley

Method

1. Combine pineapple, beetroot, apple and spring onions in a mixing bowl.

2. Sprinkle oil and vinegar over and mix thoroughly.

3. Fold in the yoghurt until well mixed.

4. Chill through and serve with any meal.

GLUTEN-FREE

GLUTEN-FREE RECIPES

67. *Muesli*

Serves 4-6

Ingredients:
4 oz (110 g) brown rice flakes
1 oz (25 g) soya bran or soya grits
3 oz (75 g) ground hazel nuts
2 oz (50 g) chopped prunes

2 oz (50 g) chopped dried apricots
2 oz (50 g) toasted sesame seeds
2 oz (50 g) pistachio nuts

Method
1.   Combine all the ingredients together.

2.   Make up with fresh fruit, fructose or raw cane sugar and milk or yoghurt.

A nutritious and delicious breakfast dish.

68. *Pea and Parsnip Soup*

Serves 4-5

Ingredients:
½ lb (225 g) parsnips – peeled and diced
½ lb (225 g) green peas
one large onion – peeled and sliced
1 pt (570 ml) water

1 teasp. yeast extract
pinch each salt and pepper
1 tablesp. soya oil

Method
1.   Soak the peas overnight, allowing room in the bowl for the peas to swell.

2.   Sauté the onion and parsnips for two minutes. Add the water and yeast extract.

3.   Drain the peas and add to the mixture. Either pressure cook for twenty minutes at 15 lbs pressure or simmer for 1½ hours until cooked (top up as necessary with cold water).

4.   Season to taste. If you prefer a smoother texture place in a blender until the desired consistency is obtained.

69. *Spinach and Watercress Soup*

Serves 4

Ingredients:

one large onion – peeled and sliced
1 tablesp. soya oil
one cooked potato or sweet potato
4-5 spinach leaves – washed and
   chopped
pinch of nutmeg

one bunch watercress – washed and
   chopped
1 pt (570 ml) vegetable water or
   water
1 teasp. yeast extract

Method

1. Sauté the onion in the soya oil until soft.

2. Place the sweet potato or ordinary potato, watercress, spinach and sautéed onion in a blender together with ½ pint (275 ml) water. Blend until smooth.

3. Transfer to a saucepan and add the remaining liquid and yeast extract.

4. Bring slowly to the boil. Pour into individual bowls and garnish with a dash of nutmeg.

70. *Pasta*

Serves 4

Ingredients:

8 oz (225 g) low gluten flour
e.g. Trufree No. 4
good pinch of salt

2 tablesp. soya oil
one egg, size 3 – well beaten
up to 3 tablesp. water

Method

1. Put the flour and salt in a bowl and add the oil. Mix together using a fork.

2. Add the well beaten egg and mix.

3. Add sufficient water to give a sticky dough.

4. Knead until smooth. You will probably need to use more flour as this mixture is rather difficult to handle.

5.   Divide into two portions and roll out each as thinly as possible. Cut into desired shapes e.g. strips, triangles or novelty shapes.

6.   Place in salted boiling water and simmer for 10-12 minutes until cooked.

7.   Drain and serve with a rich sauce (*see* below), or toss in tomato purée and serve with a meat dish.

---

71. *Rich Meat Sauce*

Serves 3-4

Ingredients:

4 oz (110 g) chicken livers – liquidised

4 oz (110 g) smoked bacon – roughly chopped

2 cloves garlic – crushed

1 medium onion – sliced

1 small pepper – diced

2 oz (50 g) mushrooms – sliced

4 tablesp. tomato purée

¼ pt (150 ml) liquid – water or stock

pinch of oregano

black pepper

salt (optional)

Method

1.   Gently fry the bacon. Add the garlic, onion and seasoning and continue to fry for 2-3 minutes.

2.   Add all the other ingredients and simmer for 20 minutes until rich and thick in consistency.

This sauce is ideal to have with freshly cooked pasta as a main course or starter.

Rich in iron and relatively low in fat and also extremely tasty.

Serve with pasta.

72. *Quick Potato Cakes*

Serves 4-6

Ingredients:

3 or 4 cold potatoes
1 egg – beaten
pinch of black pepper

enough cornmeal to make a firm
but soft dough

Method

1. Mash the potatoes well and beat in the egg and black pepper.

2. Add enough cornmeal to make a firm but soft dough.

3. Make into round flat cakes, using the cornmeal to stop the mixture sticking.

4. Grill or fry until golden brown.

73. *Stuffed Peppers*

Serves 2

Ingredients:

2 large or 4 small peppers
4 tablesp. cooked brown rice
4-6 oz (110-175 g) minced beef
1 tablesp. vegetable oil
4 tablesp. tomato purée
8 black olives

pinch each of basil and oregano
1 clove of garlic – crushed
7 fl oz (200 ml) tomato juice
8 oz (225 g) cabbage – washed and
sliced

Method

1. Sauté the minced beef in the oil and add the herbs, garlic and tomato purée. Allow to cool. Stir in.

2. Prepare the peppers by removing the stalks and seeds and then rinse.

3. Pack the prepared mixture into them.

4. Put the shredded cabbage in a casserole and place the peppers on top so that they stand up. Pour the tomato juice over them.

5. Bake until the peppers are tender and the cabbage cooked for approximately 30-35 minutes at Gas Mark 3, 325°F, 170°C.

Garnish with black olives. Serve as a complete meal.

74. *Sunshine Chicken*

Serves 4-6

Ingredients:

one 3-3½ lb (1.35-1.6 kg) roasted chicken
6-8 oz (175-225 g) brown rice (cooked weight)
one 8 oz (225 g) can sweetcorn
one small can butter beans

half a bunch watercress – washed and trimmed
stock from the chicken
4 sticks celery – diced
one medium sized pepper – diced
one orange

Method

1. Strip all the meat from the bones of the roasted chicken and chop into ½″ cubes. Place in the fridge.

2.   Boil the rice using the stock from the chicken and enough water to cover the rice. Cook until tender. Drain and allow to cool.

2.   Put the sweetcorn, butter beans, diced celery and pepper in a large bowl and mix well. Add the rice and cooked chicken. Mix thoroughly.

4.   Turn into a 10″ (25 cm) bowl and garnish with the watercress and orange segments.

75. *Pan Hagati*

Serves 2-3

Ingredients:
8 oz (225 g) back bacon – chopped
3 large potatoes – peeled and thinly
   sliced
4 oz (110 g) grated cheese

2 eggs
½ pint (275 ml) milk or yoghurt
pinch of nutmeg

Method
1.   Place the chopped bacon in an ovenproof dish and cover with the sliced potatoes.

2.   Beat the eggs in a bowl and add the milk or yoghurt and cheese. Pour this mixture over the potatoes.

3.   Sprinkle over the nutmeg.

4.   Bake at Gas Mark 4, 180°C, 350°F for 40 minutes until cooked and golden brown.

Serve with a green salad.

76. *Quick Apple Dessert*

Serves 1-2

Ingredients:
½ pint (275 ml) apple purée
1 tablesp. ground brown rice
1 egg
raw cane sugar to taste

Method

1. Beat the egg into the apple purée and add the ground brown rice.

2. Place in a saucepan and heat gently until thick. Add sugar to taste.

3. Pour into serving bowls and chill thoroughly.

Serve with yoghurt or cream.

---

77. *Mixed Fruit Crumble*

Serves 4

Ingredients:
Combine a selection of fruits to give a total weight of 1½ lbs (675 g)
e.g.
one large Bramley apple – peeled
    and sliced
one banana
4 oz (110 g) gooseberries
4 oz (110 g) blackberries
Simmer together until tender. Sweeten with honey or raw cane sugar.
Crumble:
4 oz (110 g) brown rice flour
1-2 oz (25-50g) raw cane sugar
2 oz (50 g) vegetable fat or oil
Rub the fat or oil into the flour and add the sugar.

Method

1. Place the fruit in a 2 pint (1.1 litre) oven proof dish. Allow to cool slightly.

2. Sprinkle the topping over the fruit.

3. Bake in the centre of the oven for 20-25 minutes until golden brown at Gas Mark 4, 180°C, 350°F.

Serve with yoghurt.

DESSERTS

A dessert is a final course of fruits or puddings to finish off a meal and need not necessarily be sweet. I have avoided heavy and sweet puddings and provided light, nutritious recipes and ideas for ending a meal.

DESSERTS RECIPES

DIABETIC RECIPES

78. *Banana and Strawberry Brulée*

Yoghurt contains all the calcium and protein found in fresh milk and is also very versatile for use in sweet and savoury dishes. If it is made from skimmed milk its low fat content makes it an ideal substitute for cream when trying to keep your weight under control. Bananas are a rich source of folic acid and should be one of the main fruits used in the pre-conception and pregnancy eating programme.

Serves 2-4

Ingredients:
2 large ripe bananas
1 large carton strawberry yoghurt
(15 fl oz – 425 ml)
4 tablesp. raw cane sugar
1-1½ pint (570-850 ml) ovenproof dish

Method
1.   Place the yoghurt in a mixing bowl and add the sliced bananas and stir well.

2.   Pour into the ovenproof dish.

3.   Sprinkle the sugar over the surface.

4.   Place under the grill until the sugar has caramellised, turning several times to ensure even cooking.

Serve at once – delicious, especially with a muesli biscuit.

79. *Apricot and Orange Mousse*

Serves 4-6

Ingredients:
6 oz (175 g) dried apricots
1 orange jelly
1 can evaporated milk or plamil
   soya milk (14 oz – 400 g)
1 egg white

115

Method

1.   Soak the apricots in water overnight, and then simmer gently until tender.

2.   Allow the apricots to cool and then chop into bite size pieces. Put to one side.

3.   Using the liquid from the apricots make up the jelly to ¾ pint (425 ml). Put to one side.

4.   Whisk the egg white in a clean bowl until stiff. Put to one side.

5.   Put the jelly and apricots in a large mixing bowl and mix together. Add the milk, and then finally fold in the egg white, ensuring that all the ingredients are well mixed.

6.   Pour into a 2 pint (1.1 litre) glass bowl and put in the fridge to set, preferably overnight.

Delicious, especially on a hot summer's day.

---

80. *Sugar-Free Fruit and Nut Gingerbread*

Research has shown that babies are born with a "sweet tooth" and are indifferent to sour, salty and bitter tastes, which are developed later. It is therefore important to develop a "savoury tooth" when a baby is weaned.

Ingredients:

12 oz (350 g) wholemeal flour	½ pint (275 ml) coconut milk
2 level teasp. ground ginger	(ordinary milk will do)
2 level teasp. cinnamon	2 eggs, size 2 – beaten
2 level teasp. bicarbonate of soda	6 oz (175 g) sultanas
8 oz (225 g) vegetable fat	4 oz (110 g) flaked almonds
8 oz (225 g) black strap molasses	

Method

1.   Line a roasting tin measuring 13″ x 10″ (32cm x 25cm).

2.   Mix the flour, spices and bicarbonate of soda thoroughly and place in a mixing bowl.

3.   Melt the fat and black strap molasses – do not allow to boil.

4.   Pour the melted mixture into the mixing bowl, add the milk, beaten eggs, sultanas, flaked almonds and mix well, using a metal spoon.

5.   Pour into the prepared tin and bake for 50-60 minutes at Gas Mark 3, 325°F, 170°C, until firm to the touch.

6.   Allow to cool. Wrap in greaseproof paper and eat the next day.

To give a slight variation use a combination of 4 oz (110 g) rye flour, 4 oz (110 g) barley flour and 4 oz (110 g) wholemeal flour. With the natural sweetness of the ingredients you hardly notice the omission of sugar. This gingerbread is a good source of nutrients, contains a minimum of calories and provides a useful filling if you feel a little nauseous during the day.

---

81. *Mixed Berry Royale*

Fruits and vegetables add bulk to our diets. They help us feel "full" after a meal without us having to resort to foods more concentrated in calories.

Serves 6-8

Ingredients:

1 punnet of strawberries	juice of half a lemon
1 punnet of raspberries	enough water to make the fruit
8 oz (225 g) cherries	pulp up to 2 pints (1.1 litre)
two 1 pint (570 ml) sachets of	
gelatine	

Method

1.   Wash and trim the fruit, destone the cherries (keeping six to eight back for decoration).

2.   Place the fruit and lemon juice in a liquidiser or food processor and make a pulp.

3.   Transfer the pulp to a measuring jug and top up with water to make 2 pints (1.1 litre).

4.   Dissolve the gelatine as described for Fizzy Grapefruit (*see* page 120) and add it to the pulp, stirring well.

5.   Transfer to a wetted 2 pint (1.1 litre) jelly mould and allow to set, preferably overnight.

6.   Remove by gently easing the contents away from the mould onto a wetted plate.

Decorate with the cherries and serve with junket, cream or ice-cream.

82. *Banana and Walnut Tea Ring*

Serves 4-6

Ingredients:
8 oz (225 g) wholewheat flour
1 heaped teasp. baking powder
1 oz (50 g) raw cane sugar
2 oz (50 g) butter or margarine
1 medium sized banana (roughly chopped)

1 oz (25 g) chopped walnuts
¼ pint (150 ml) milk

Topping:
2 tablesp. raw cane sugar

Method
1. Mix the flour and baking powder together in a mixing bowl.
2. Rub in the fat.
3. Stir in the sugar, chopped banana and walnuts.
4. Mix to a soft dough with the milk.
5. Knead gently on a floured surface and shape into a circle approximately 9″ (23 cm) and ¾″ (2 cm) in depth.

6. Place on a greased baking sheet.

7. Using a sharp knife mark into 8 sections, brush with water or milk and sprinkle with the 2 tablesp. of sugar.

8. Bake for 30-35 minutes on the top shelf of the oven at Gas Mark 6, 400°F, 200°C, until well risen and the topping is crunchy.

9. Divide into sections when cold and then split and butter.

Delicious!

83. *Orange and Banana Mix*

This quick dessert is ideal for pregnant women because oranges and bananas are rich in folic acid, Vitamin C and other trace elements. Folic acid is particularly important as it is so easily destroyed and needs to be eaten daily, so as well as having this dessert you could make oranges and bananas your snack between meals or whilst relaxing during the evening.

Serves 1-2

Ingredients:
1 large or two small oranges
1 large banana
dash of lemon juice

6 tablesp. fruit juice – any variety will do
3 tablesp desiccated coconut – roasted

Method
1. Peel the orange and segment it. Place in a serving dish and add the lemon juice and fruit juice.

2. Peel and chop the banana. Add to the orange mix and stir.

3. Top with the toasted coconut and serve.

84. *Malted Rice Pudding*

Adding malt to any dish improves its nutritional value and provides those all important B vitamins which help soothe nerve endings.

Ingredients:

2 oz (50 g) pudding or Carolina rice
2 oz (50 g) raw cane sugar
¼ teasp. vanilla essence

1 pint (570 ml) milk – cow's or
  goat's
1 heaped tablesp. extract of malt

Method

1.   Wash the rice under a running tap and place in a 1½ pint (850 ml) ovenproof dish.

2.   Pour the milk over the rice.

3.   Stir in the sugar, vanilla essence and extract of malt.

4.   Place on the lowest shelf of the oven and cook at Gas Mark 3, 325°F, 170°C, for 50-60 minutes.

Serve either hot or cold – my family like it with a serving of fresh raspberries.

85. *Fizzy Grapefruit Jelly*

As ordinary table jellies are high in sugar, flavourings and colourings, I would urge you to make your own. This delicious recipe is quick, simple and nutritious.

An adult needs at least 30 mgs of Vitamin C every day. Unfortunately Vitamin C is easily destroyed by heat and light. Vitamin C is important for the health of the body's connective tissue and helps in wound healing. It cannot be easily stored in the the body and must therefore be consumed daily. That is why it is important to eat fresh fruit and vegetables each day.

Serves 4

Ingredients:

one carton of frozen, concentrated
  grapefruit juice (defrosted)
enough carbonated mineral water
  to make the juice up to 1 pint
  (570 ml) – Perrier type

one fresh grapefruit
4 sprigs mint leaves
one 1 pint (570 ml) jelly mould
1 sachet of gelatine sufficient to set
  one pint (570 ml) of liquid

Method
1.   To dissolve the gelatine place four tablesp. of cold water in a cup, and then sprinkle the gelatine over the water. Place ½ pint (275 ml) of water in a saucepan and stand the cup in the water (like a bain marie). Heat the saucepan and stir the gelatine mix from time to time until dissolved.

2.   In a measuring jug place the defrosted grapefruit juice and enough carbonated mineral water to make it up to one pint (570 ml).

3.   Add the dissolved gelatine and stir well.

4.   Pour onto a wetted mould and leave in the fridge until set (overnight is best).

5.   Turn onto a wetted plate (so that you can easily move the mould should you have positioned it incorrectly) and decorate with fresh grapefruit segments and washed mint leaves.

---

86. *Cottage Cheese on Toast with Sliced Melon*

Contains four units carbohydrate.

Although an unusual combination of foods, these ingredients really do go well together providing a delicious contrast in flavour and texture. I liked it for breakfast when I was pregnant. It is rich in protein provided by the wholemeal bread and cottage cheese and low in fat because the toast is not buttered. The fresh melon slices give a delicate flavour to make it a good meal to start the day.

Serves 1

Ingredients:
2 small thin slices wholemeal bread
3 oz (75 g) carton of cottage cheese
1 generous slice honeydew melon

Method
1.   Simply toast the bread. Pile on the cottage cheese and top with the sliced melon pieces.

– And if you really want to be spoilt, get someone to make it for you and bring it up to bed to you.

87. *Lentil and Vegetable Pie* – *with cheesy topping*

Contains 13 units Carbohydrate.

Serves 4

Ingredients:
10 tablesp. lentils, brown or yellow
1 tablesp. soya oil
one large onion, sliced
one large courgette, sliced
two medium green peppers, sliced
one clove of garlic
½ teasp. dill seed
pinch black pepper

Topping:
four sticks celery, well chopped

14 oz (400 g) mashed potatoes
3 oz (75 g) mature cheddar cheese,
    grated
four tablesp. natural thick set
    yoghurt
(approx. half 5 oz carton)

Garnish:
three tomatoes, sliced and arranged
    on top

Method

1. Wash the lentils and either pressure cook for 20 minutes at 15 lbs pressure or cook for 45 minutes in ample water until soft.

2. Heat the oil in a frying pan, add the garlic, onion, courgette, green pepper, dill seed and black pepper. Continue to sauté until the vegetables are tender (about 10 minutes).

3. Mash the lentils until quite smooth and stir in the vegetables. Transfer to a 2-3 pint oven proof dish.

Topping:

4. Mash the potatoes, then add the yoghurt and beat well. Stir in the cheese and chopped celery.

Pile on the topping, smooth and garnish with the tomato slices and bake for 25-30 minutes at 300°F, 150°C.

Serve with a green salad made up of several types of lettuce.

---

88. *Liver and Mixed Vegetable Casserole*

Contains five units Carbohydrate.

Serves 2

Ingredients:

8 oz (220 g) calf's liver	½ pint (250 ml) stock - vegetable
4 sticks celery	3 tablesp. tomato purée
2 oz (50 g) button mushrooms	2 teasp. vegetable oil
6-8 oz (160-200 g) turnips	black pepper
2 tablesp. worcester sauce	salt (optional)

Method

1. Cut the liver into 2″ strips. Trim the vegetables and slice the celery and turnips and mushrooms into bite sized pieces.

2. Heat the oil and sauté the liver for 2 minutes.

3. Add the worcester sauce, stock, tomato purée, salt and pepper and simmer gently for 10 minutes.

4. Place in a moderate over 170°C, 325°F, Gas Mark 3, and cook for a further 45 minutes until tender and until most of the liquid has evaporated.

Serve with jacket potatoes.

89. *Diabetic Jelly – Rhubarb and Orange*

This is low in calories and therefore the carbohydrate content is negligible (no units carbohydrate).

Serves 4

Ingredients:
one sachet unflavoured gelatine – enough to set 1 pint (500 ml) liquid
½ pint (250 ml) water

¼ pint (125 ml) diabetic orange squash
8 oz (220 g) unsweetened stewed rhubarb

Method
1.   Dissolve the gelatine as described in Fizzy Grapefruit Jelly (*see* page 120).
2.   When thoroughly dissolved combine the water, squash and stewed rhubarb in a mixing bowl.
3.   Pour into individual serving bowls and allow to set in the fridge.

90. *Sugar-Free Blackcurrant and Nut Crumble*

Contains seven units carbohydrate.

Serve 4

Ingredients:
1 lb (450 g) blackcurrants
4 level tablesp. wholemeal flour
1 oz (25 g) low calorie margarine
2 oz (50 g) ground almonds

Method
1.   Cook the blackcurrants in a little water – just enough to make the fruit tender and to stop it sticking.

2.   Place in a 2 pint (1.1 litre) oven proof dish. Allow to cool.

3.   Place the wholemeal flour in a mixing bowl. Rub in the margarine and stir in the coconut.

4.   Sprinkle over the blackcurrants and bake until golden brown for 35 minutes at Gas Mark 3, 325°F, 170°C.

N.B. Always check that these foods are suitable for you and are part of your daily allowance. Ask your doctor if not sure.

DRINKS

Drinks that are nutritious are an important part of a healthy diet, especially when you are breast feeding, as your needs increase. A drink is often a good way of warding off sickness, especially fizzy drinks – but not the sugary type.

DRINKS

91. *Lemon and Lime Cooler*

Ingredients:

1 lemon – juice plus grated rind
2 limes – juice plus grated rind
6 teasp. raw cane sugar (optional)

1 pint (½ litre) boiling water
fizzy mineral water (chilled)
fresh mint leaves to garnish

Method

1. Place juice and rind into heat proof jug.

2. Pour on the boiling water and leave until cool.

3. Strain.

4. To serve: pour into tall glasses, top up with fizzy mineral water and decorate with the fresh mint leaves.

92. *Winter Warmer*

Ingredients:

2 pints (1 litre) still grape juice
½ lemon – sliced
½ orange – sliced

1 cinammon stick
2-3 cloves
2 heaped tablesp. fresh cranberries

Method

1. Place all ingredients into a saucepan and heat gently.

2. Serve in a punch bowl for special occasions. Add some sugar if you have a sweet tooth.

93. *Appleade*

Serves 3

Ingredients:

3 large dessert apples (Cox's or
  Granny Smiths)
1 pint (600 ml) boiling water
1 teasp. raw cane sugar

Method

1. Liquidise or finely chop the apples and place in a bowl.

2. Pour onto the boiling water, add the sugar and leave to stand for 30 mins.

3. Strain into a jug and allow to cool.

4. To serve: pour over ice cubes and decorate glass with apple slices.

94. *Soya Yoghurt Cup*

Serves 4

Ingredients:
1 pack unsweetened soya milk
1 large carton strawberry yoghurt
4-8 strawberries (trimmed and

washed)
4-8 cocktail sticks
4 tablesp. crushed ice

Method

1. Place soya milk and yoghurt into a blender or food processor. Blend until smooth.

2. Place 1 tablesp. crushed ice into a glass and pour over the soya mixture.

3. Complete with a strawberry on a cocktail stick and serve.

Nutritious as well as delicious.

95. *Melon Floater*

Serves 6

Ingredients:
½ red melon (watermelon)
¼ cucumber
1 tablesp. crushed ice

Method

1. Using a baller make twelve melon balls. Put to one side.

2. Remove brown pips and liquidise the melon.

3.   Strain and pour into a large jug.

4.   Slice the cucumber, cut halfway into each piece so that they stand on the side of the jug.

5.   Just before serving add the crushed ice and float the melon balls on the prepared juice.

Extremely thirst quenching in hot weather – or as a starter to a dinner party.

96. *Cantaloupe Cup*

Ingredients:

1 medium ripe cantaloupe, coarsely chopped
¼ pt (150 ml) milk
½ pt (300 ml) yoghurt

½ lime, squeezed
2 tablesp. raw cane sugar (optional)

Method

1.   Place all ingredients in a blender and blend until smooth.

2.   Serve immediately in chilled glasses.

Drinks for Entertaining

You do not have to put alcohol into a drink to make it taste delicious. Here are some ideas: tell your guests it's a "mocktail".

97. *French Flower*

Serves 1 (add extra as needed)

Ingredients:
1 wine glass sparkling apple juice
2 dashes Angostura bitters
1 teasp. sugar

Method
Shake or stir together and decorate with lemon slices.

131

98. *Snow White*

Serves 1

Ingredients:

1 measure pineapple juice
1 measure orange juice
1 measure lime juice

1 dash grenadine
soda water to top

Method

Shake ingredients over ice and pour into tall glasses. Top up with soda water.

99. *Tropical Lady*

Serves 1

Ingredients:

1 wine glass tropical fruit juice
1 small banana
dash lemon juice
1 teasp. desiccated coconut

Method

Blend juices and banana. Pour into a cocktail glass and sprinkle desiccated coconut on top.

100. *Calypso Cream*

Ingredients:

1 wine glass milk (any type)
1 small banana
dash lemon juice

1 teasp. ground almonds
3 teasp. crushed ice

Method

Blend milk, banana and lemon juice. Pour onto crushed ice and sprinkle ground almonds on top.

101. *Bells of Saint Clements*

Ingredients:
1 measure freshly squeezed orange juice
1 measure freshly squeezed lemon juice
3 dashes Angostura bitters
sparkling mineral water to top up

Method
Shake all ingredients over ice and top with the mineral water.

Serve with a straw or a fancy umbrella.

102. *Egg Nog*

Ingredients:
2 large fresh eggs
dash Angostura bitters
top of the milk or 4 tablesp. soya milk.

Method
Blend very well until rich and creamy and pour over a little crushed ice.

REFERENCES

1. "Congenital permanent diabetes mellitis and coeliac disease", Hatterig G. et al, *J. Pediatr.*, 1982, Dec 10 (6) 955-7
2. "Coeliac disease fertility and pregnancy", Ferguson R. et al, *Scand. J. Gastroenterol*, 1982, Jan 17th (1) 65-68
3. "Foods for patients with coeliac disease", Campbell J. A., *Can. Med. Assoc. J.* 1982, Nov 15th 127(10) 963-5
4. *Recent advances in perinatal medicine*, edited by Malcolm L. Chiswick, Churchill Livingstone
5. "The diabetic pregnancy" – a perinatal perspective, Irwin R. Merkatz and Peter A. J. Adam
6. *The Manual of Nurtition*, Ministry of Agriculture and Fisheries
7. *Chemical composition of foods*, McCance and Widdowson

N.B. *The Manual of Nutrition* and *Chemical Composition of Foods* have been used for all nutritional calculations

INDEX